Key Stage 3
Developing Numeracy

HANDLING DATA

ACTIVITIES FOR TEACHING NUMERACY

year 8

Hilary Koll and Steve Mills

A & C BLACK

Contents

Published 2004 by A & C Black Publishers Limited
37 Soho Square, London W1D 3QZ
www.acblack.com

ISBN 0-7136-6478-9

Editors: Lynne Williamson and Marie Lister

The data on pages 34, 35 and 45 is taken from www.statistics.gov.uk and www.homeoffice.gov.uk/rds.

The authors and publishers would like to thank David Chadwick, Corinne McCrum and Jane McNeill for their advice in producing this series of books.

Printed in Great Britain by St Edmundsbury Press Ltd, Bury St Edmunds, Suffolk.

A & C Black uses paper produced with elemental chlorine-free pulp, harvested from managed sustainable forests.

Introduction

Key Stage 3 Developing Numeracy: Handling Data is a series of photocopiable resources for Years 7, 8 and 9, designed to be used during maths lessons. The books focus on the Handling Data strand of the Key Stage 3 National Strategy *Framework for teaching mathematics*.

Each book supports the teaching of mathematics by providing a series of activities that develop essential skills in numeracy. The activities aim to reinforce learning and develop the skills and understanding explored during whole-class teaching. Each task provides practice and consolidation of an objective contained in the framework document. On the whole the activities are designed for pupils to work on independently, either individually or in pairs, although occasionally some pupils may need support.

The activities in **Handling Data Year 8** relate to the following topics:
- specifying a problem, planning and collecting data;
- processing and representing data, using ICT as appropriate;
- interpreting and discussing results;
- probability.

How to use this book

Each double-page spread is based on a Year 8 objective. The spread has three main sections labelled A, B and C, and ends with a challenge (**Now try this!**). The work grows increasingly difficult from A through to C, and the 'Now try this!' challenge reinforces and extends pupils' learning. The activities provide the teacher with an opportunity to make informal assessments: for example, checking that pupils are developing mental strategies, have grasped the main teaching points, or whether they have any misunderstandings.

This double-page structure can be used in a variety of ways: for example, following whole-class teaching the pupils can begin to work through both sheets and will experience gradually more complex questions, or the teacher can choose the most appropriate starting points for each group in the class, with some pupils starting at A and others at B or C. This allows differentiation for mixed-ability groups. 'Now try this!' provides a greater challenge for more able pupils. It can involve 'Using and Applying' concepts and skills, and provides an opportunity for classroom discussion. Where appropriate, pupils can be asked to finish tasks for homework.

The instructions are presented clearly to enable the pupils to work independently. There are also opportunities for pupils to work in pairs and groups, to encourage discussion and co-operation. A calculator icon indicates the parts of the activities in which calculators should be used. Where there is no icon, the teacher or pupils may choose whether or not to use them. Brief notes are provided at the foot of each page to assist the pupil or classroom assistant, or parent if the sheets are used for homework. Remind the pupils to read these before beginning the activity.

In some cases, the pupils will need to record their workings on a separate piece of paper, and it is suggested that these workings are handed in with the activity sheets. The pupils will also need to record their answers to some of the 'Now try this!' challenges on another piece of paper.

Organisation

Very little equipment is needed, other than rulers, sharp pencils, protractors, calculators and squared paper. The pupils will also need graphical calculators or access to ICT equipment for some of the activities.

To help teachers select appropriate learning experiences for pupils, the activities are grouped into sections within the book to match the objectives in the Key Stage 3 National Strategy *Yearly teaching programmes*. However, the activities do not have to be used in the order given. The sheets are intended to support, rather than direct, the teacher's planning.

Some activities can be made easier or more challenging by masking or substituting some of the numbers. You may wish to re-use some pages by copying them onto card and laminating them, or by enlarging them onto A3 paper. They could also be made into OHTs for whole-class use.

Teachers' notes

Further brief notes, containing specific instructions or points to be raised during the first part of the lesson, are provided for particular sheets (see pages 6–7).

Whole-class oral and mental starters

The following activities provide some practical ideas to support the main teaching part of the lesson, and can be carried out before pupils use the activity sheets.

Specifying a problem, planning and collecting data

Letters in your name

Pose some questions that require the pupils to gather information about the number of letters in the full name of people in the class. Discuss what information would be necessary to say whether the following statements are true or false:

- *More than half the people in our class have fewer than 20 letters in their name.*
- *Less than one-quarter of the people in our class have 23 letters or more in their name.*

Collect the raw data and ask questions about the mode, median and mean number of letters in a full name. Discuss ways of sorting or representing the data (for example, by grouping it into equal class intervals). Sort the data and talk about how this is helpful for interpreting it. The modal group can then be found.

Processing and representing data

Correlation situations

Call out two sets of values in which correlation may or may not be present (see examples below). Ask the pupils to say whether they think there is correlation, and if there is, whether the correlation is positive or negative, and strong or weak.

Marks in science test	Marks in music test
Intelligence	Length of your arm
Outdoor temperature	Number of hot drinks drunk
Outdoor temperature	Sales of cold drinks
Size of electricity bill	Number of hours of sunshine each day
Height	Weight
Average speed travelled	Time
Height above sea-level	Air temperature
Sales of breakfast cereal	Advertising costs
Number of cars on the road	Accident rate
Size of household gas bill	Outdoor temperature

What's possible?

Choose four, five or six 0–9 digit cards. Display them on the board, with one face down and the others face up, for example:

Discuss what the **mode** of the cards could be, for example:

- *Could the mode be 3? What would the hidden card have to be?*
- *Could the mode be 2? Explain your thinking.*
- *Could the modes be 2, 3 and 6? Could the mode be 2 but not 6?*
- *For each possible digit that the hidden card could show, what would the mode of the cards be?*

Discuss what the **median** of the cards could be, for example:

- *Could the median be: 2? 2.5? 3? 4.5? 5? 6? 7? What would the hidden card have to be?*
- *For each possible digit that the hidden card could show, what would the median of the cards be?*

Discuss what the **mean** of the cards could be, for example:

- *If the mean of the cards is an integer (a whole number), what could the hidden card be? Is there another answer?*
- *What is the highest possible mean?*
- *What is the lowest possible mean?*
- *Is the mean 3.75 possible?*

Repeat using different digit cards.

Interpreting and discussing results

On a roll

Split the class into two teams. Ask a pupil from Team A to roll a dice ten times; write the results on the board. Ask Team A to find the mode (or modal values), the median, the mean and the range. Repeat the experiment for Team B. For each average or range, award a point to the team with the highest number. Award an extra point if the pupils can say which of the averages best represents the data, and why.

Probability

Names in the hat

Each pupil should write their first name on a small piece of paper. Place all the names in a hat and tell the pupils that you are going to draw one name from the hat. Ask the pupils to estimate or work out the probability that the name pulled out:

- *will be theirs*
- *will begin with the letter J*
- *will have seven letters*
- *will have fewer than five letters*
- *will have at least two letters the same.*

Test the theoretical probabilities by pulling names out of the hat (replacing each name before you draw another one). Discuss the relationship between the theoretical and experimental probabilities.

Teachers' notes

Specifying a problem, planning and collecting data

Pages 8 & 9

This activity explores different ways of collecting data, through conducting surveys, doing experiments or using secondary sources. Encourage the pupils to think of different questions and to consider which people should be surveyed, or how an experiment could be conducted. Stress that careful planning of experiments and surveys is necessary.

Pages 10 & 11

Discuss the various aspects of questionnaires, including how information is recorded and which options are given. Remind the pupils that the category 'other' is often used where listing all possible options would be too extensive. In part C, encourage discussion in pairs or small groups.

Pages 12 & 13

For the 'Now try this!' challenge, the pupils will need access to newspapers or magazines.

Pages 14 & 15

The pupils will need to collect data from the whole class for some parts of this activity. Discuss the meaning of the term 'two-way table' and encourage the pupils to describe advantages of this type of table: for example, it allows you to examine relationships between two different criteria. Demonstrate on the board how to complete a two-way table, such as a table showing heights of males and females in the class (males in one column and females in the other), with class intervals for appropriate heights as row headings. Ensure that the pupils understand the notation $1.4 \leq h < 1.5$; discuss that 1.5 would be recorded in the group $1.5 \leq h < 1.6$. For part C, the pupils will need to find out how far they live from school. Provide maps of the local area (or the pupils could use www.multimap.com).

Pages 16 & 17

Before beginning this activity, you could ask the pupils to think about the differences between questionnaires (which are completed personally by each person taking part in the survey) and data collection sheets (which are completed by one person or a group on behalf of those being surveyed). Discuss the advantages and disadvantages of both types of survey. These could include difficulty in reading handwriting, amount of resources used, amount of time taken, and so on.

Processing and representing data, using ICT as appropriate

For all activities which involve representing data, the pupils can be asked to use graphical calculators or ICT equipment to draw graphs and charts.

Pages 18 & 19

Revise the mean during the first part of the lesson, using small values that can be added mentally. Demonstrate how to find the sum and then divide by the number of values in the list. Before the pupils begin part B, discuss how to find the mean value of a set of data arranged in a frequency table. In this case, the pupils need to first multiply each score by the number of pupils and find the total number of points scored. Then they divide this by the total number of pupils. Once they have completed part C, you could ask individuals to explain the method for calculating means using an assumed mean to the rest of the class.

Pages 20 & 21

Revise the mode, median, mean and range during the first part of the lesson. The mode is the most frequently occurring item or value, and the median is the value in the middle when the numbers are arranged in order. Make sure that the pupils remember to reorder the numbers when finding the median. Discuss that different types of average are useful for different purposes: for example, staff in a clothes shop need to know the modal size or sizes, as this tells them which sizes to stock in greater quantities. The median size would not be a useful average in this case. Discuss the situations on these pages during the plenary and ask the pupils to suggest which average is best in each case. When finding the median of information in a table, the pupils need to know how to find the middle position in a set of numbers. Demonstrate this using an example: if there are ten values, the middle position is halfway between the 5th and 6th values. Show that there are four numbers in the list, then the 5th and 6th values, and then four more numbers. For the 'Now try this!' challenge, the pupils will need recent football results from a newspaper or the Internet.

Pages 22 & 23

Demonstrate how to draw stem-and-leaf diagrams: first list several two-digit numbers on the board. Ask the pupils to look at the tens digit of each number and to write these digits in order vertically, from largest to smallest, to form a stem. Explain that the units digits should be arranged in ascending order, with the smallest nearest the stem, in line with the correct tens digit. These diagrams can be useful for examining and comparing sets of data, as they make it easier to find the median and the mode.

Pages 24 & 25

First ask the pupils to give the number of degrees in a full turn (360) and explain that when pie charts are constructed using protractors, it is necessary to know the total number of units (in this case, people) that the whole pie represents. Explain that dividing 360° by this total gives the number of degrees that each unit (person) will represent: for example, in a pie chart representing 90 people, 360° ÷ 90 = 4°, therefore each person will be represented by 4°. Multiplication is then used to find the size of a sector representing several people. Remind the pupils to check that their angles total 360° before beginning construction. The pupils will require protractors, and will need to be confident in using them to draw angles about a point (revise this, if necessary).

Pages 26 & 27

Encourage the pupils to discuss the scales they will use when constructing these bar charts. The charts can be constructed on graph paper or using ICT.

Pages 30 & 31

Discuss how to draw scatter graphs by plotting points and exploring any patterns the points might form. The pupils will need to consider a suitable scale for the graph in part A. During the plenary session, use the term 'correlation' to describe a positive or negative relationship between values (for example, where one value increases as the other increases, or where one value increases as the other decreases).

Pages 32 & 33

Remind the pupils of the notation used in part A for grouping data: for example, $140 \leq h < 145$. Ensure they appreciate that 145 would be recorded in the group $145 \leq h < 150$.

Interpreting and discussing results

Pages 34 & 35

In part C, discuss the fact that the two graphs do not cover identical areas: one covers both the North Sea and Northeast Atlantic, whilst the other covers only the North Sea. Invite the pupils to suggest the implications of this. Further information and other related data can be found on the National Statistics website at www.statistics.gov.uk.

Pages 36 & 37

Discuss that pie charts are useful for displaying proportions. In the examples in part A, it is impossible to say the *number* of phones sold by each company unless the total number of phones is given.

Pages 38 & 39

More information and other related data can be found on the National Statistics website at www.statistics.gov.uk.

Pages 42 & 43

Ensure the pupils understand that the clutch size is the number of chicks hatched at the same time in one nest. Revise how to find the different averages (mean, median and mode) from lists of values. Encourage the pupils to discuss the implications of different modes, means and medians, and help them to appreciate that one might be better than the others for different situations.

Pages 44 & 45

Page 45 can be used on its own, without page 44. The pupils could be asked to interpret the graphs and to write a report on the information. In pairs or groups, they could give a presentation to encourage clear communication of ideas and findings. Other data on this topic can be found on websites such as www.statistics.gov.uk or www.homeoffice.gov.uk/rds.

Pages 46 & 47

A large amount of data regarding tourism in the UK can be found on the website www.staruk.org.uk.

Probability

Pages 50 & 51

The term 'mutually exclusive' can be introduced, if appropriate. Discuss that two events that are mutually exclusive (for example, 'a club' and 'not a club') have a probability total of 1.

Pages 52 & 53

Dominoes are *not* required for these pages. In part C, the pupils are given the opportunity to use and apply their understanding of probability.

Pages 56 & 57

For parts A and B, provide one pack of cards per eight pupils, so that each pair can use one suit (13 cards). In this activity, the pupils explore the link between theoretical probabilities and those based on experiments. Encourage them to describe the differences during the plenary session. For part C, each pair will need a large sheet of paper (A3 would be suitable) and a matchstick or cocktail stick.

Pages 58 & 59

For part A, discuss with the pupils that their fractions should be out of 48, because they are looking at 48 balls (not 49). The National Lottery is an area to which pupils – and adults – may find it difficult to apply theoretical probability. Encourage the pupils to discuss their ideas about probability, in particular their answers to question C1. Emphasise that theoretically any number combination is just as likely to occur as any other – including 1, 2, 3, 4, 5, 6 or the same numbers as last week. More information and recent lottery results can be found on the website www.lottery.co.uk.

Data-day living

A Explain **where** you would conduct a survey to help you answer these questions. Decide **whom** you would ask.

(a) Do people prefer to shop at out-of-town complexes or in town centres?

_____

_____

(b) How much TV do young people and adults watch?

_____

_____

(c) What types of books are most popular with elderly people?

_____

_____

(d) What is the most popular type of fast-food for different ages?

_____

_____

B For each problem, suggest related questions that you could investigate. Then say how you would go about finding the information.

(a) What is the average number of games played in a tennis match?

- _Are there differences between men's and women's tennis?_
- _Where can I find the data I need?_

I would look on the Internet or teletext for some tennis results. I would organise the data to show the number of games in each match, for men and for women. I would find the mean average number of games.

(b) Are more people born in August than in any other month?

- _____
- _____

_____

(c) A friend tells you that her favourite pizza place is better value for money than the others in the area. How could you find out if this is true?

- _____
- _____

_____

There are three main ways of collecting data:
(i) conduct a survey by asking people questions;
(ii) do an experiment by measuring or counting;
(iii) look in books or magazines, or on the Internet (use **secondary** sources).
Methods (i) and (ii) use **primary** sources. Method (iii) uses **secondary** sources.

8

Data-day living

C

1. Describe what **experiment** you would organise to help you answer these questions. Give as much detail as you can.

(a) How high can people reach with a single standing jump (beginning with both feet on the ground)?

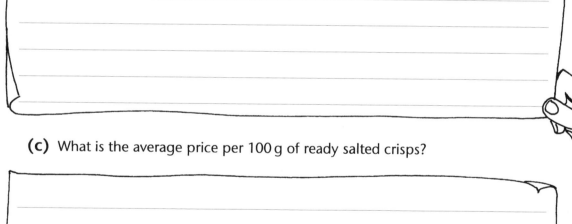

(b) Which is the most common car colour?

(c) What is the average price per 100 g of ready salted crisps?

2. Discuss your answers with a partner.

NOW TRY THIS!

● Devise and carry out an experiment to answer this question:

Which newspaper uses the most words on its front page?

There are three main ways of collecting data:
(i) conduct a survey by asking people questions;
(ii) do an experiment by measuring or counting;
(iii) look in books or magazines, or on the Internet (use **secondary** sources).
Methods (i) and (ii) use **primary** sources. Method (iii) uses **secondary** sources.

Question quality

A Read these two questionnaires.
One is much better than the other.

> **Questionnaire**
> Do you go on holiday?
> How often do you go on holiday?
> For how long do you go on holiday?
> Where do you go on holiday?
> What is your favourite type of holiday?

1. Do you go on holiday?   yes ☐   no ☐
   (If no, stop survey now.)

2. How often do you go on holiday?
   once a year ☐   twice a year ☐   three times a year ☐
   less than once a year ☐   other _____

3. For about how many weeks a year do you go on holiday?
   less than 1 week ☐   1 week ☐
   2 weeks ☐   more than 2 weeks ☐

4. What are your favourite holiday destinations? (Tick as many as you like.)
   Britain ☐   France ☐   Spain ☐   Greece ☐
   Italy ☐   Canaries ☐   USA ☐   Australia ☐

5. What is your favourite type of holiday? _____

Give reasons why the second questionnaire is better. _____
_____
_____
_____

B **(a)** Ruby is asked to fill in the second questionnaire. Explain why she will find it difficult.

> I go on holiday about five times a year, but mainly just for weekends. Some years I go to Ireland for a fortnight to see my relatives, if I can afford it.

_____
_____
_____

(b) On a separate sheet of paper, rewrite the questionnaire so that Ruby will find it easier to fill in. Make sure that these people can record their information, too.

> I don't go on holiday every year but when I do, I like to go for six weeks or so.

> I spend my holidays at my sister's in Skegness. Sometimes I have a day trip to France in spring.

> We like to go hiking in Switzerland, but often we don't go on holiday at all.

To write a good questionnaire, you need to think about what information you would like to find out, and what types of answers people might give.

Question quality

C A library manager wants to find out more information about the people using the facilities. Her questionnaire is not very easy to work with.

Questionnaire
What are you here to borrow?
How often do you visit?
Do you borrow CDs and videos?
What type of books do you like?
How old are you?

(a) Discuss with a partner how these people might fill in the questionnaire.

I come here about once a week, usually to borrow a novel. I'd rather not tell you my exact age. I don't have a CD-player.

I visit the library about once a month. I usually end up paying a fine as I'm often late returning my books and DVDs.

I come to the library to read the papers. I'm not a member of the library.

I work here at the library. I wish we had more money to spend on DVDs and videos. I'm 28.

I've just returned three books which were for my son's homework. I'm in my forties. I come here now and again to use the Internet.

I bring my children (aged 5 and 9) to borrow books twice a week. I don't read much. I'm 30.

(b) Write a better questionnaire that will be easier to fill in and will give clearer information.

Plan the questionnaire on scrap paper first! **!**

NOW TRY THIS!

- Write a questionnaire that will help you to find out these things:

  Do most people like sport?
  How often do people play sport?
  What are their favourite sports?
  Do most people prefer playing sport or watching sport?

 To write a good questionnaire, you need to think about what information you would like to find out, and what types of answers people might give.

Developing Numeracy
Handling Data
Year 8
© A & C BLACK

11

The right people

A Each of these statements is going to be investigated. A sample of people has been chosen to help with the survey or experiment. Say whether you think the sample is a good one and explain your answer. If you think the sample is not a good choice, suggest a better one.

(a) The local train service is unsatisfactory.

Sample: car drivers on their way to work

(b) Smoking should not be allowed in public places.

Sample: smokers in the street

(c) Advertising is good for business.

Sample: every tenth business in Yellow Pages

(d) Wearing seatbelts prevents injuries.

Sample: nurses in a hospital

B A survey or experiment is going to investigate each of these statements. Suggest a good sample of people.

Sample

(a) Vegetables are nicer from a greengrocer than from a supermarket.

(b) Taking vitamin tablets is good for the health of elderly people.

(c) Cleaning your teeth twice a day prevents tooth decay.

 When you conduct a survey, you shouldn't just ask people who are directly involved with the issue, as this may not give a valid result. There may be other groups of people or experts who can give more accurate information.

Developing Numeracy
Handling Data
Year 8
© A & C BLACK

C What experiment or survey would you carry out to test each of these claims? Describe the sample you would choose and explain what you would do.

(a) **Kills all known germs!**

(b) **Lowest mobile phone rates**

(c) **Computers — cheaper here than anywhere!**

(d) **This tastes better than butter!**

(e) **We offer the best service**

(f) Only 5% of our trains leave late. 95% leave on time!

NOW TRY THIS!
- With a partner, look through newspapers or magazines. Find five adverts that make a claim about a product or service. Suggest how you would test each claim.

When you conduct a survey, you shouldn't just ask people who are directly involved with the issue, as this may not give a valid result. There may be other groups of people or experts who can give more accurate information.

Two-way tables

A The two-way table below is designed to help you answer this question:

Collect the data for pupils in your class.

In our class, are people who own a pet more likely to be vegetarians?

Use tallying to record the responses.

!

	Owns a pet	Does not own a pet
Vegetarian		
Not a vegetarian		

Not reconstituted Soya mince again!

Dinner, Fido

B Work in a group.

(a) Choose *one* of the questions below. Plan how you will go about answering it. Devise a two-way table.

In our class, are girls more likely to have a mobile phone than boys?

In our class, are people with older brothers or sisters more likely to enjoy sports than those who don't have older brothers or sisters?

In our class, are people born in the months of September to February taller than those born in March to August?

In our class, are people who have blue eyes more likely to play a musical instrument than people who have brown eyes?

(b) Collect the data by asking the pupils in your class.

(c) Look at the data and answer the question. Explain your findings.

_____

_____

_____

A **two-way table** lets you see the relationship between two things: for example, in part A you can record how many vegetarians own a pet/don't own a pet and how many non-vegetarians own a pet/don't own a pet.

Developing Numeracy
Handling Data
Year 8
© A & C BLACK

Two-way tables

C This **two-way table** is designed for collecting data to help answer this question:

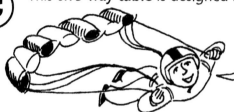

Is it true to say that people who live furthest from school come by car or bus (or other motorised vehicle) and people who live closest to school cycle or walk?

Distance (d) from school (km)	Method of transport						
	Walk	**Cycle**	**Car**	**Bus**	**Coach**	**Train**	**Other**
$0 \leq d < 0.5$							
$0.5 \leq d < 1$							
$1 \leq d < 1.5$					*		
$1.5 \leq d < 2$							
$2 \leq d < 2.5$							
$2.5 \leq d < 3$							
$3 \leq d$							

(a) One of the cells in the table has an asterisk (*). Explain what information would go here.

_____

_____

(b) Collect the data for pupils in your class. Use tallying to record the responses in the table.

If people use more than one method of transport, record only the main one. **!**

(c) Look at the data you have collected and answer the question. Explain your findings.

_____

_____

(d) Do you think this is enough data to be sure of your answer? Why?

_____

_____

NOW TRY THIS!

Do young people listen to more music than older people?

- Design a two-way table which will let you record people's ages and how much time they spend listening to music. Use **grouped data** for both the age and the time spent listening to music.

Remember to use groups of equal size. **!**

 A **two-way table** lets you see the relationship between two things. When you use **grouped data**, think carefully about which group to put the values in: for example, 0.5 km should go in $0.5 \leq d < 1$. In this group, d (the distance) is greater than or equal to 0.5. In the group $0 \leq d < 0.5$, d is *less than* 0.5.

Developing Numeracy
Handling Data
Year 8
© A & C BLACK

15

Talking rubbish!

Work in a group.

You are going to design a questionnaire to find out the type of recycling that residents of your local area carry out, and how often they recycle.

In your group, discuss the key issues that you will include in the questionnaire.

- Think about the different types of recycling, such as:

paper   plastic   ink cartridges   disposable nappies   clothes

glass   food waste (compost)   aluminium   books   cardboard

- Think about the different ways of recycling, such as:

bottle banks   charity shops   compost bins

household collection   second-hand bookshops

- Think about whether people recycle:

occasionally   once a week   when passing a recycling site

when collected from the door   only for certain items   never

1. When you have discussed the key issues, write your questionnaire.

Plan the questionnaire on scrap paper first! !

2. What should the sample size be? How could you conduct this survey?

 Sometimes it is a good idea to give people their own questionnaires to fill in. In other situations it might be easier if you (or a group of you) collect data by asking people directly. Think about which method would be best for this project.

**Developing Numeracy
Handling Data
Year 8
© A & C BLACK**

Talking rubbish!

C Work in a group.

You are going to design a | data collection sheet | to find out how important people feel the issue of recycling is. You should investigate whether those who feel most strongly live in cities/towns or in villages/the countryside.

1. **(a)** In your group, discuss the key issues that you will include in your data collection sheet.

   • Consider the categories you could use for how strongly people feel, for example:

very strongly, strongly…   on a scale of 1 to 5…

   • Think about how you will arrange the sheet so that you can tell whether each response is from a resident of a city/town or village/countryside. (You could use a two-way table.)

   (b) When you have discussed these issues, design your data collection sheet.

   (c) What should the sample size be? How could you conduct this survey?

2. Conduct a survey of pupils in your class using your data collection sheet. Write a report of your findings.

NOW TRY THIS!

An organisation wants to make people more aware of the effects of air pollution. It decides to conduct a survey to encourage people to think about this issue.

• Design a questionnaire that people could fill in on paper and post back, or could complete online on the organisation's website.

 Sometimes it is a good idea to give people their own questionnaires to fill in. In other situations it might be easier if you (or a group of you) collect data by asking people directly. When you do this, the sheet you record on is called a **data collection sheet**.

You gotta mean it

A

Each diagram shows the numbers of passengers in the carriages of a train. Find the ⬚mean⬚ number of passengers per carriage.

(a)

36	48	18	43	28	56	33	30	14

Mean = _____

(b)

55	30	42	28	21	16	32	42	34	44	30

Mean = _____

(c)

52	53	57	33	32	25	27	11	37	31	12	20

Mean = _____

(d)

41	39	31	40	42	11	13	48

Mean = _____

(e)

46	33	52	11	9	77	43	30	21	27	46	61	8

Mean = _____

B

Pupils from around the UK took part in a maths challenge.
Each pupil was asked eight questions.

1. This frequency table shows the numbers of pupils with different scores.

(a) Complete the table.

Score	0	1	2	3	4	5	6	7	8	Total
Number of pupils	6	12	43	39	56	67	58	16	3	
Number of points scored	0	12	86							

⟨0 × 6⟩ ⟨1 × 12⟩ ⟨2 × 43⟩

(b) Use the table to find the mean score, to two decimal places (2 d.p.). _____

2. These tables show the results for previous years. Complete each table and find the mean score to 2 d.p.

(a)

Score	0	1	2	3	4	5	6	7	8	Total
Number of pupils	0	3	17	78	79	88	91	5	1	
Number of points scored										

Mean score = _____

(b)

Score	0	1	2	3	4	5	6	7	8	Total
Number of pupils	2	6	17	15	85	96	4	0	0	
Number of points scored										

Mean score = _____

(c)

Score	0	1	2	3	4	5	6	7	8	Total
Number of pupils	8	11	17	56	63	68	89	53	8	
Number of points scored										

Mean score = _____

To calculate the **mean** of a set of values, find the total of all the values and then divide by the number of values in the set. When data is arranged in a frequency table, use multiplication to help you find the information you need to calculate the mean.

Developing Numeracy
Handling Data
Year 8
© A & C BLACK

You gotta mean it

C Read this method of finding the **mean** mentally.

> Find the mean of 48.6, 51.2, 52.1, 49.9 and 50.2

- Look at the values and choose an easy number that lies somewhere in the middle. Call this the 'assumed mean'. **50.0**
- Find the difference between each number and the assumed mean. Use the positive or negative sign to show whether the number is more or less.
  ⁻1.4,   +1.2,   +2.1,   ⁻0.1,   +0.2
- Find the total of all these differences. (Watch out – this might be negative!) **+2.0** Then divide this by the number of values. **2.0 ÷ 5 = 0.4**
- Finally, add this to your assumed mean. This is the **actual** mean. **50.4**

1. 🖩 Now use a calculator to find the mean. Do you get the same answer?

2. Use the strategy above to answer these questions mentally. Show your workings.

(a) Find the mean of
24.6, 24.3, 26.1, 25.3 and 25.7

(b) Find the mean of
15.7, 17.3, 16.3, 16.8 and 15.9

(c) Find the mean of
63.2, 63.8, 61.4, 62.8 and 61.8

(d) Find the mean of
37.6, 39.5, 38.2, 37.4 and 37.7

3. 🖩 Check your answers. Find the mean using a different method.

NOW TRY THIS!

The mean of five numbers is 32.5.
Here are four of the numbers: 33.1, 31.2, 29.5, 32.8, _____

- Use an assumed mean to help you find the fifth number.
- Set another challenge like this for a partner to solve.

 The **mean** can be found in different ways. The most common way is to find the total of all the values and divide by the number of values.

The best average

A

Ronnie O'Connor is a snooker player. These are his scores in a tournament.

1. Find the **range**, **mode**, **median** and **mean** for his scores in each round.

Round 1		Round 2		Semi-final		Final	
Game	Score	Game	Score	Game	Score	Game	Score
1	16	1	74	1	106	1	73
2	85	2	104	2	87	2	6
3	103	3	17	3	58	3	81
4	26	4	17	4	17	4	76
5	73	5	85	5	19	5	87
6	9	6	38	6	4	6	0
7	73	7	67	7	103	7	1
		8	17	8	87	8	52
		9	67	9	113	9	107
						10	52
						11	147

Round 1	Round 2	Semi-final	Final
Range _____	Range _____	Range _____	Range _____
Mode _____	Mode _____	Mode _____	Mode _____
Median _____	Median _____	Median _____	Median _____
Mean _____	Mean _____	Mean _____	Mean _____

2. Which type of average do you think best represents Ronnie's performance in each round of the tournament? Explain your answer. _____

_____

_____

B

This list shows the approximate mass of some woodland birds.

Type	Mass (g)
Dunnock	20
Goldcrest	6
Blue tit	11
Robin	17
Greenfinch	27
Wood pigeon	300
Treecreeper	9
Great tit	27
Chaffinch	30
Wren	10
Chiffchaff	8
Pheasant	600

1. What is the range of measurements? _____

2. Find: **(a)** the mode _____

(b) the median _____

(c) the mean _____

3. Which type of average do you think best represents this set of values?

_____

4. Explain why you chose this average and not the others. _____

_____

 To find the **range**, subtract the lowest value from the highest value. Remember, the **mode** is the most common value. The **median** is the middle value when the values are arranged in order. If there are two values in the middle, the median is halfway between the two. To calculate the **mean**, find the total of all the values and divide by the number of values.

Developing Numeracy
Handling Data
Year 8
© A & C BLACK

The best average

These charts show the types of job that people do in six sports stores, and the number of people who do each type of job. The charts also show how much they earn each day.

1. Work out how much the people earn in total each day. Complete the charts.

SUPERSPORTS

Cleaners (£25)	Assistants (£42)	Managers (£83)	Total
3	6	1	10
£75	£252	£83	£410

Bats'n'Balls

Cleaners (£28)	Assistants (£46)	Managers (£100)	Total
5	9	1	

Sportsavers

Cleaners (£31)	Assistants (£59)	Managers (£124)	Total
12	15	3	

Sports 4 U

Cleaners (£24)	Assistants (£29)	Managers (£105)	Total
4	5	2	

Focusports

Cleaners (£26)	Assistants (£54)	Managers (£101)	Total
8	7	2	

Firstchoice Sports

Cleaners (£22)	Assistants (£32)	Managers (£205)	Total
4	3	2	

2. (a) Find the **range**, **mode**, **median** and **mean** for each store.

Supersports	Bats'n'Balls	Sportsavers
Range £58 Mode £42	Range ____ Mode ____	Range ____ Mode ____
Median £42 Mean £41	Median ____ Mean ____	Median ____ Mean ____
Sports 4 U	**Focusports**	**Firstchoice Sports**
Range ____ Mode ____	Range ____ Mode ____	Range ____ Mode ____
Median ____ Mean ____	Median ____ Mean ____	Median ____ Mean ____

(b) Which type of average do you think best shows the average pay for Bats'n'Balls? Why?

_____

(c) Which type of average best shows the average pay for Firstchoice Sports? Why?

_____

NOW TRY THIS!

- Find the weekend football results in a newspaper. Draw frequency tables to show the number of goals scored in each match in the Premiership and one other league division.
- Find the range, mode, median and mean for each division. Describe any differences.

Remember, the **mode** is the most common value. The **median** is the middle value when the values are arranged in order. To find the **mean** wage, calculate the total amount of money earned in wages and divide by the number of people. In the 'Now try this!' challenge, use tallying in your frequency tables.

Heads of state

A A [stem-and-leaf diagram] can be useful for comparing data. This stem-and-leaf diagram plots the data by using the tens digits in the stem and the units digits as the leaves.

Age at death of presidents of the USA from 1789 to 1869

67 90 83 85 73 80 78 79 68 71 53 65 74 64 77 56 66

stem	leaf
9	
8	
7	
6	4 5 6 7 8
5	

(a) Complete the diagram by writing each units digit alongside the correct tens digit. Arrange the units digits in ascending order, with the smallest nearest the stem.

(b) Describe what this diagram tells you about the most common ages at which presidents died. _____

B **1.** Plot these two sets of data on this stem-and-leaf diagram.

Age at death of presidents of the USA

1789–1869

67 90 83 85 73 80 78 79 68 71 53 65 74 64 77 56 66

1869–1974

70 49 57 71 67 58 60 72 67 57 60 90 63 88 78 46 64

> This time, use both sides of the stem to show the two sets of data.

1789–1869			1869–1974
		9	
		8	
		7	
		6	
	6 3	5	
		4	

2. For each set of data, find the:

(a) range _____   range _____

(b) mode (or modal values) _____   mode (or modal values) _____

(c) median _____   median _____

In a **stem-and-leaf diagram**, the units digits should be arranged in ascending order. Always start with the smallest nearest the stem. This makes it easier to find the **mode** and the **median**. Remember, the mode is the most common value. The median is the middle value when the values are arranged in order.

Developing Numeracy
Handling Data
Year 8
© A & C BLACK

Heads of state

C

1. Plot these two sets of data on this **stem-and-leaf diagram**.

Length of reigns of the last 40 British kings and queens (to the nearest whole number of years)

1272–1685

36 24 22 44 5 0 18 6 38 24 2 0 22 39 9 13 22 50 20 35

1685–1952

15 1 25 9 63 7 10 59 33 13 12 6 13 3 36 24 22 6 13 3

1272–1685		1685–1952
	0	

2. For each set of data, find the:

(a) range _____   range _____

(b) mode _____   mode _____

(c) median _____   median _____

3. Write a description comparing the two sets of data.

_____

_____

_____

_____

• Draw a stem-and-leaf diagram for these two sets of data.

Length of the index fingers of boys and girls in a class

Boys	**Girls**
61 mm, 68 mm, 72 mm, 61 mm, 76 mm,	75 mm, 63 mm, 80 mm, 57 mm, 59 mm,
75 mm, 72 mm, 77 mm, 56 mm, 74 mm	80 mm, 69 mm, 85 mm, 66 mm, 51 mm

• Write a report about the data. Include the range and averages.

In a **stem-and-leaf diagram**, the units digits should be arranged in ascending order. Always start with the smallest nearest the stem. This makes it easier to find the **mode** and the **median**. Remember, the mode is the most common value. The median is the middle value when the values are arranged in order.

Money, money, money

A

A group of 120 twelve-year-old girls were asked to say what they spent the largest part of their pocket money on. The data is shown in the table below.

(a) If the data was shown as a | pie chart |, how
many degrees would represent each person? _360°_ ÷ _____ = _____

(b) Work out how many degrees would represent each activity or item. Complete the table.

Activity or item	Number of girls	Calculation	Angle of sector
Going out	26	_26 ×_ ___ = ___	___ °
CDs, videos, DVDs	25		
Clothes	23		
Toiletries	12		
Sports and hobbies	27		
Other	7		

(c) Check that the angles of all your sectors have a total of **360°**.

(d) Now show this data in the first pie chart below. Use a protractor.

12-year-olds 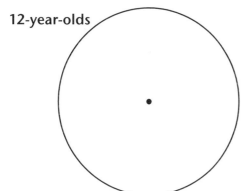   **14-year-olds**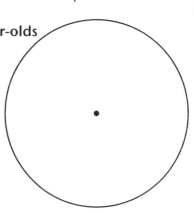

B

1. This data shows the results for 120 fourteen-year-old girls.
Complete the table. Then show the data in the second pie chart.

Activity or item	Number of girls	Calculation	Angle of sector
Going out	33	_33 ×_ ___ = ___	___ °
CDs, videos, DVDs	28		
Clothes	24		
Toiletries	22		
Sports and hobbies	7		
Other	6		

2. On a separate piece of paper, write a report comparing the two pie charts. Describe the differences between spending habits of twelve- and fourteen-year-old girls.

 A **pie chart** is a circle divided into sectors so that the areas of the sectors represent the data. Colour each sector of the pie chart a different colour and label it. When you draw the second pie chart, make sure that you use the same colours as you did for the first. This makes it easier to compare the information.

Developing Numeracy
Handling Data
Year 8
© A & C BLACK

Construct pie
charts for
categorical data

C

1. A group of 100 twelve-year-old boys were asked to say what they spent the largest part of their pocket money on. The data is shown in the table below.

   (a) If the data was shown as a pie chart, how
   many degrees would represent each person? ___360°___ ÷ _____ = _____

   (b) Work out how many degrees would represent each activity or item. Complete the table.

Activity or item	Number of boys	Calculation	Angle of sector
Going out	18	18 × _____ = _____	_____ °
CDs, videos, DVDs	9		
Clothes	7		
Computer games	11		
Sports and hobbies	45		
Other	10		

   (c) Check that the angles of all your sectors have a total of **360°**.

   (d) Now show this data in the first pie chart below. Use a protractor.

12-year-olds 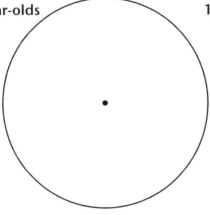   **14-year-olds**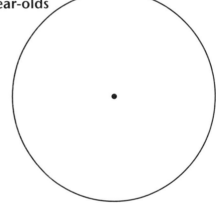

2. This data shows the results for 100 fourteen-year-old boys. Show the data in the second pie chart above.

3. On a separate piece of paper, write a report comparing the two pie charts. Describe the differences between spending habits of twelve- and fourteen-year-old boys.

Activity or item	Number of boys
Going out	23
CDs, videos, DVDs	13
Clothes	18
Computer games	15
Sports and hobbies	29
Other	1

NOW TRY THIS!

- Collect data on the spending habits of 30 girls and 30 boys. Draw a pie chart for each. Then compare the results.

Colour each sector of the pie chart a different colour and label it. When you draw the second pie chart, make sure that you use the same colours as you did for the first. In your report, you should state what proportion of the people surveyed spent their money on each category. The proportions could be written as fractions, decimals or percentages.

Hot or not?

A These tables show the average temperatures in degrees Celsius (°C) each month in Plymouth and in Aberdeen.

Plymouth, England

Jan	Feb	Mar	Apr	May	Jun	Jul	Aug	Sep	Oct	Nov	Dec
6.0	6.0	6.9	9.1	11.8	14.6	16.2	16.2	14.5	11.5	8.4	6.8

Aberdeen, Scotland

Jan	Feb	Mar	Apr	May	Jun	Jul	Aug	Sep	Oct	Nov	Dec
3.2	3.4	4.5	6.3	8.8	11.8	13.6	13.4	11.5	8.7	5.6	3.9

1. On graph paper or using a computer, draw a bar chart to show these temperatures. For each month, draw two bars next to each other, one for Plymouth and one for Aberdeen. Use different-coloured bars for each city.

2. **(a)** During which month (or months) is there the greatest difference in temperature between Plymouth and Aberdeen?

   _____

   (b) During which month (or months) is there the smallest difference in temperature between Plymouth and Aberdeen?

   _____

   (c) Describe similarities and differences between the temperatures in the two cities. Suggest possible reasons for these.

   _____

   _____

   _____

B 1. In Plymouth, during which month is the temperature:

(a) 5.4°C warmer than in April? _____

(b) 9.3°C colder than in August? _____

2. In Aberdeen, during which month is the temperature:

   (a) 5.5°C warmer than in January? _____

   (b) 7.9°C colder than in June? _____

3. Estimate what the average temperature might be on 1st June. Explain your answer.

   _____

   _____

 When you choose a scale for a **bar chart**, look carefully at the values and remember that the highest value has to fit on your scale. On this bar chart, make sure that the highest temperature is somewhere towards the top of your scale.

**Developing Numeracy
Handling Data
Year 8**
© A & C BLACK

Hot or not?

C These tables show the average temperatures in degrees Celsius (°C) each month in Scarborough and in Riyadh.

Scarborough, England

Jan	Feb	Mar	Apr	May	Jun	Jul	Aug	Sep	Oct	Nov	Dec
4.0	4.3	5.6	7.6	10.2	13.4	15.4	15.2	13.5	10.2	6.8	4.6

Riyadh, Saudi Arabia

Jan	Feb	Mar	Apr	May	Jun	Jul	Aug	Sep	Oct	Nov	Dec
14.3	16.2	20.8	25.0	30.8	33.6	34.6	34.4	31.4	26.3	20.6	15.4

1. On graph paper or using a computer, draw a bar chart to show these temperatures. For each month, draw two bars next to each other, one for Scarborough and one for Riyadh. Use different-coloured bars for each location.

2. **(a)** During which month is there the greatest difference in temperature between Scarborough and Riyadh?

   (b) During which month is there the smallest difference in temperature between Scarborough and Riyadh?

   (c) Describe similarities and differences between the temperatures in the two places. Suggest possible reasons for these.

3. Estimate from your bar chart what the average temperature in Riyadh might be on the 1st of each month. Discuss your estimates with a partner.

> Find the average of consecutive months.

Jan	Feb	Mar	Apr	May	Jun	Jul	Aug	Sep	Oct	Nov	Dec

NOW TRY THIS!

This data shows the average monthly rainfall (in mm) in Scarborough and in Riyadh.

- Show this information on *one* bar chart.

- Write a report about the weather in both locations using the data on this page.

	Jan	Feb	Mar	Apr	May	Jun	Jul	Aug	Sep	Oct	Nov	Dec
Scarborough	57.7	47.3	46.3	46.8	52.7	55.1	64.6	69.0	58.6	68.3	64.9	61.5
Riyadh	13.8	10.4	29.8	29.7	13.1	0.0	0.0	0.0	0.0	0.7	4.5	11.3

When you choose a scale for a **bar chart**, look carefully at the values and remember that the highest value has to fit on your scale. On this bar chart, make sure that the highest temperature is somewhere towards the top of your scale.

Developing Numeracy
Handling Data
Year 8
© A & C BLACK

Home sweet home

1. This table shows the average house price in the UK between 1992 and 2002.

Year	Average house price
1992	£64 000
1993	£62 500
1994	£62 750
1995	£61 700
1996	£64 500
1997	£68 500
1998	£72 200
1999	£77 400
2000	£85 000
2001	£92 250
2002	£108 300

(a) Draw axes and label the horizontal axis with the years. Label the vertical axis from £50 000 to £110 000.

(b) Plot this data on a line graph . Join each point to the next with a straight line.

(c) Describe the shape of the line and what it shows.

_____

_____

_____

2. (a) On the same line graph, plot this data for the average house price in Scotland during the same period. Use a different colour to draw the lines.

Year	Average house price
1992	£55 800
1993	£56 800
1994	£57 700
1995	£57 700
1996	£59 300
1997	£59 200
1998	£60 700
1999	£61 500
2000	£62 000
2001	£63 600
2002	£69 000

(b) Describe the shape of the line and what it shows.

_____

_____

_____

(c) Compare the average house prices of Scotland and the whole of the UK. List similarities and differences.

_____

_____

_____

Source: www.hbosplc.com

3. In which year was the average house price in Scotland:

(a) closest to the UK figure? _____   (b) furthest away from the UK figure? _____

4. What was the greatest price increase in one year in:

(a) the UK? _____   (b) Scotland? _____

(a) Draw axes and label the horizontal axis with the years from 1992 to 2002. Label the vertical axis from £0 to £110 000.

(b) Plot both sets of data above on these axes.

(c) Compare this line graph with the one you drew in part A. Describe what differences you notice.

_____

_____

You should join the points on these **line graphs** with straight lines (rather than a curve) to make it easier to see trends. Points can be joined with a curve if you are sure that all the intermediate points along the curve represent real information.

Developing Numeracy
Handling Data
Year 8
© A & C BLACK

Home sweet home

C

1. These tables show the average house price in Northwest England and in Northern Ireland between 1992 and 2002.

Northwest England

Year	Average house price
1992	£57 800
1993	£56 100
1994	£55 200
1995	£53 200
1996	£53 900
1997	£55 400
1998	£56 400
1999	£59 000
2000	£62 000
2001	£65 450
2002	£74 900

Northern Ireland

Year	Average house price
1992	£37 400
1993	£39 000
1994	£41 700
1995	£44 400
1996	£52 600
1997	£54 200
1998	£60 600
1999	£64 000
2000	£68 000
2001	£76 300
2002	£79 000

(a) Plot this data on a line graph. Join each point to the next with a straight line. Use a different colour for each location.

(b) Describe the shapes of the lines and compare the average house prices. List similarities and differences. _____

_____

_____

_____

2. In which year was the average house price in Northwest England:

(a) closest to the Northern Ireland figure? _____

(b) furthest away from the Northern Ireland figure? _____

3. What was the greatest price increase in one year in:

(a) Northwest England? _____

(b) Northern Ireland? _____

4. (a) In which year did houses become more expensive in Northern Ireland than in Northwest England?

_____

(b) Why might this have happened?

_____

5. Is it true to say that house prices in Northern Ireland doubled between 1992 and 2002? _____

6. By approximately how many per cent have house prices in Northwest England risen between 1992 and 2002? _____

NOW TRY THIS!

In 2002, the average house price in Wales was £77 600.

- Is it possible to estimate the average house price in Wales in 1992, using the data above? Give reasons for your answer. Explain anything you have assumed to be true.

You should join the points on this **line graph** with straight lines (rather than a curve) to make it easier to see trends. Points can be joined with a curve if you are sure that all the intermediate points along the curve represent real information.

Developing Numeracy
Handling Data
Year 8
© A & C BLACK

Scatterbrain

A

(a) This table shows the number of cold drinks sold per hour at a shop, according to the outside temperature. Draw a $\boxed{\text{scatter graph}}$.

Temperature (°C)	0	4	8	12	16	20	24	28	32	36
Number of cold drinks sold each hour	1	3	6	11	19	28	35	41	48	58

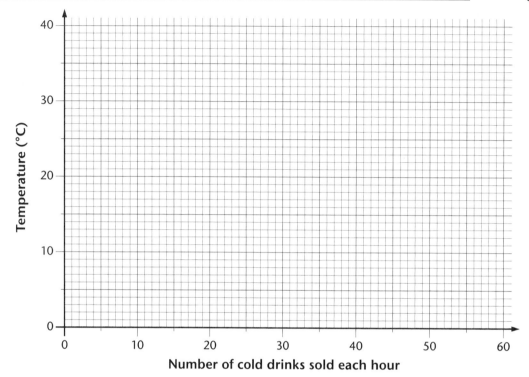

Temperature (°C) — vertical axis (0, 10, 20, 30, 40)

Number of cold drinks sold each hour — horizontal axis (0, 10, 20, 30, 40, 50, 60)

(b) Do the dots on the scatter graph form a pattern? _____

(c) Describe what your graph tells you about the number of drinks sold. _____

_____

B Do the dots on each scatter graph form a pattern? Write what this tells you about each graph.

(a) _____ *Yes* _____

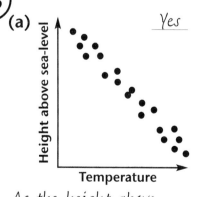

Height above sea-level

Temperature

As the height above
sea-level increases, _____

(b) _____

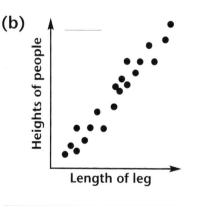

Heights of people

Length of leg

_____

_____

(c) _____

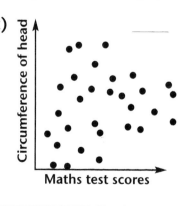

Circumference of head

Maths test scores

_____

_____

When you draw a **scatter graph**, don't join the points with lines. A scatter graph shows whether there is a connection between two sets of values. If there is a connection, it might be that one value gets larger as the other gets larger. Or, one value may get smaller as the other gets larger.

Developing Numeracy
Handling Data
Year 8
© A & C BLACK

Scatterbrain

C

1. This list shows the average duration of pregnancy and typical lifespan of some animals.

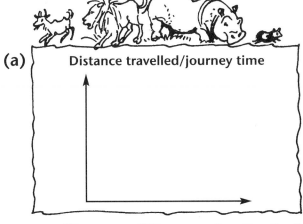

Animal	Duration of pregnancy (days)	Typical lifespan (years)
Bear	240	22
Deer	250	15
Donkey	365	20
Goat	150	12
Guinea pig	60	5
Hamster	17	2
Hippo	250	30
Horse	340	25
Lion	110	10
Mouse	25	2
Rat	21	3
Sheep	150	12

(a) On graph paper or using a computer, draw a **scatter graph** to show this information.

(b) Do the dots form a pattern? _____

(c) What might this tell you about the relationship between the average duration of pregnancy and typical lifespan of different animals?

_____

_____

_____

_____

2. Sketch what you think a scatter graph would look like for these values.

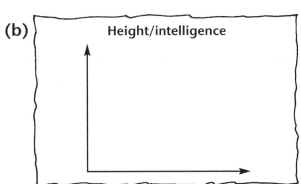

(a)   Distance travelled/journey time

(b)   Height/intelligence

(c)   Size of home gas bill/outside temperature

(d)   Distance travelled/amount of fuel used

3. Discuss your graphs with a partner.

● Think of three more pairs of values that you could plot on a scatter graph. Write what the patterns might look like. Explain what this would tell you about the relationship.

 If the points on a scatter graph are spread diagonally from bottom left to top right, this shows a **positive correlation** (one value gets larger as the other gets larger). If the points are spread diagonally from top left to bottom right, this shows a **negative correlation** (one value gets smaller as the other gets larger). A random spread of points shows **zero correlation**.

New heights

A

The heights in centimetres of some pupils are shown.

154,	148,	154,	149,	155,	162,	150,	163,	152,	164,
148,	151,	158,	145,	147,	153,	159,	159,	161,	144,
145,	150,	160,	149,	152,	155,	150,	155,	146,	159

! Cross off each number from the list as you tally.

1. Find the **range** of these heights. _____

2. Complete this frequency table. Group the data into ⌐ equal class intervals ⌐.

Height (*h*) in centimetres	Tally	Frequency
140 ≤ h < 145		
145 ≤ h < 150		
150 ≤ h <		

3. Find the total number of pupils (check both the list of heights and the table). _____

4. What is the **modal class**? _____

5. Do you think all the pupils might be of a similar age? Explain your answer.

_____

_____

B

1. Complete this ⌐ frequency diagram ⌐ for the data in your frequency table.

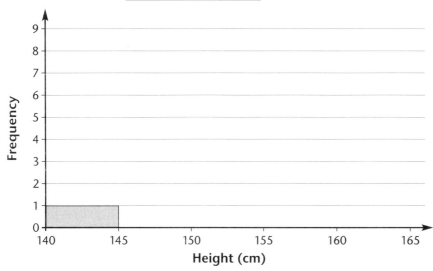

2. How many pupils' heights are:

(a) less than 150 cm? _____   **(b)** 155 cm or greater? _____

 When you use grouped data, think carefully about which group to put the values in: for example, 145 cm should go in 145 ≤ *h* < 150. In this group, *h* (the height) is greater than or equal to 145. In the group 140 ≤ *h* < 145, *h* is *less than* 145. Make sure you use groups of equal size (these are called **equal class intervals**). The **modal class** is the most common group.

Developing Numeracy
Handling Data
Year 8
© A & C BLACK

New heights

C This frequency diagram shows the number of pupils scoring different percentages in a maths test.

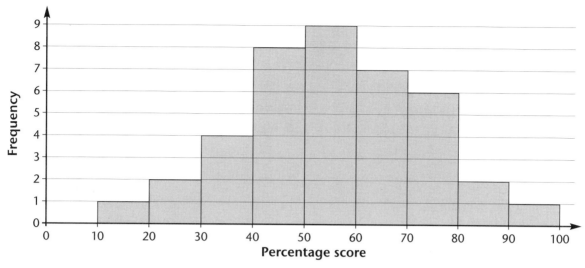

1. How many pupils took the test in total? _____

2.

   On this diagram, more than half of the pupils scored less than 55%.

   Do you think this statement is true or false, or is more information needed? Explain your answer.

   _____

   _____

3.

   On this diagram, the range of the scores is 90%.

   Do you think this statement is true or false, or is more information needed? Explain your answer.

   _____

   _____

4. Is the following statement true or false? _____

     The bars in this diagram represent intervals of $0 \leq P < 10$, $10 \leq P < 20$, and so on, where P is the percentage score.

5. One pupil's score has been missed off the frequency diagram. She scored 70%. Add this information to the diagram by extending one of the bars.

NOW TRY THIS!

- Draw a frequency diagram for these percentage scores.
- Write six true statements about the information in your diagram.

Percentage (P)	Frequency
$0 \leq P < 20$	5
$20 \leq P < 40$	16
$40 \leq P < 60$	22
$60 \leq P < 80$	31
$80 \leq P \leq 100$	11

 When you use grouped data, think carefully about which group to put the values in: for example, 70% should go in $70 \leq P < 80$. In this group, 'P' (the percentage) is greater than or equal to 70. In the group $60 \leq P < 70$, 'P' is *less than* 70.

Something fishy

A This bar chart shows the number of million tonnes of cod in the North Sea and Northeast Atlantic in the years 1977 to 1996.

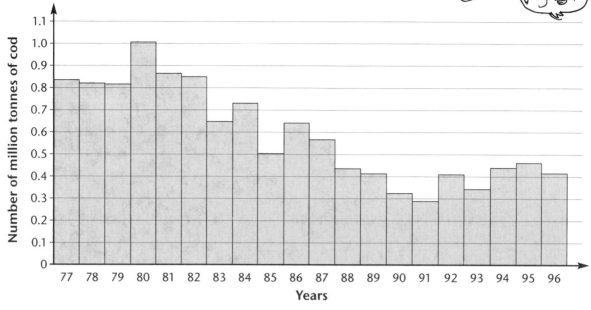

1. Estimate how many million tonnes of cod there were in:

   (a) 1978 _0.82_   **(b)** 1985 _____

   (c) 1988 _____   **(d)** 1995 _____

2. During which year (or years) was the number of million tonnes of cod:

   (a) about 0.65? _____   **(b)** about 0.29? _____

   (c) about 0.57? _____   **(d)** about 0.33? _____

3. What was: **(a)** the maximum amount of cod recorded? _____

   (b) the minimum amount of cod recorded? _____

B 1. In which three consecutive years were cod numbers about the same?

   _____

2. What happened to cod numbers during the years:

   (a) 1980 to 1990? _____

   (b) 1992 to 1996? _____

3. What do you think might affect cod numbers? _____

   _____

   _____

4. In which year could the following statement have been made? _____

   The number of million tonnes of cod has about halved in the last six years.

 Look carefully at the scale on the bar chart and make sure you understand what each axis is showing.

**Developing Numeracy
Handling Data
Year 8
© A & C BLACK**

Something fishy

Interpret bar charts and draw inferences

C This bar chart shows the number of million tonnes of cod in the North Sea and Northeast Atlantic in the years 1977 to 1996.

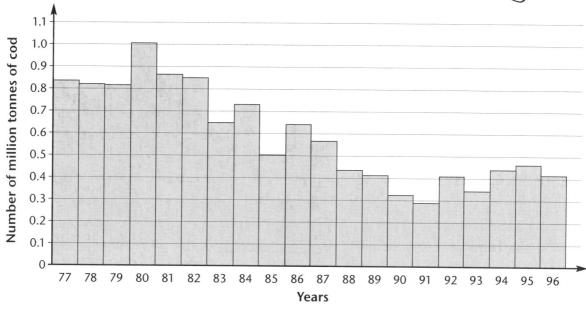

1. Look at the cod numbers. Between which two years was there:

   (a) the largest increase? _____ **(b)** the largest decrease? _____

   (c) the smallest increase? _____ **(d)** the smallest decrease? _____

2. About how many more million tonnes of cod were there in:

   (a) 1980 than 1990? _____ **(b)** 1977 than 1987? _____

3. This graph shows the number of thousand tonnes of cod caught in the North Sea during the same years.

   Compare the two graphs and write what you notice. Suggest reasons for the features you describe.

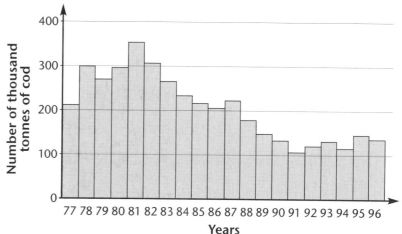

_____

_____

NOW TRY THIS!

• In 1997, there were 0.6 million tonnes of cod in the North Sea and Northeast Atlantic. About how many cod would you expect to be caught in the North Sea that year?

Look carefully at the scale on the bar chart and make sure you understand what each axis is showing.

Developing Numeracy Handling Data Year 8 © A & C BLACK

35

Easy as pie

A These pie charts show the proportions of different makes of mobile phones sold in 2000 and 2002.

2000

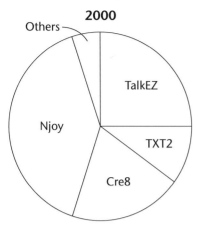

Others — TalkEZ, Njoy, TXT2, Cre8

2002

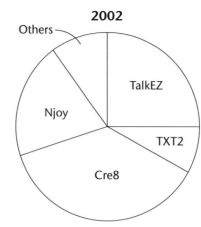

Others — TalkEZ, Njoy, TXT2, Cre8

1. Which mobile phone company had the greatest number of sales in:

(a) 2000? _____   (b) 2002? _____

2. In 2000, approximately what **percentage** of sales were from:

(a) TalkEZ? _____   (b) TXT2? _____   (c) Cre8? _____

(d) Njoy? _____   (e) others? _____

3. In 2002, approximately what **fraction** of sales were from:

(a) TalkEZ? _____   (b) TXT2? _____   (c) Cre8? _____

(d) Njoy? _____   (e) others? _____

B **1.** Are these statements true? For each one, write **true**, **false** or **can't tell**.

(a) TXT2 sold more phones in 2000 than in 2002.

(b) Njoy sold fewer phones in 2002 than in 2000.

_____   _____

(c) Cre8 had a larger proportion of the total sales in 2000 than in 2002.

(d) In 2000, fewer Cre8 phones were sold than Njoy phones.

_____   _____

(e) In 2002, more TXT2 phones were sold than TalkEZ phones.

(f) In 2002, about three times as many TXT2 phones were sold as Cre8 phones.

_____   _____

2. Is it true to say that TalkEZ sold the same number of phones in 2000 as in 2002?

Explain your answer. _____

When you estimate a percentage of a pie chart, remember that the whole is 100%, half is 50%, and so on. To estimate fractions, it is useful to imagine the pie split into equal sectors (for example, if it is split into five equal sectors, each sector is one-fifth, or 20%).

**Developing Numeracy
Handling Data
Year 8**
© A & C BLACK

Easy as pie

C These pie charts show the proportions of different makes of mobile phones sold in 2000 and 2002.

2000

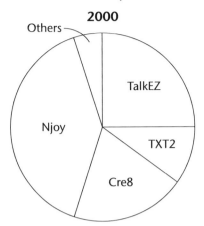

Others, TalkEZ, Njoy, TXT2, Cre8

2002

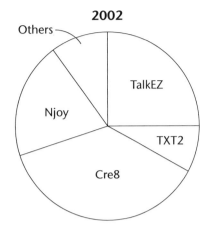

Others, TalkEZ, Njoy, TXT2, Cre8

1. Complete this table to show the approximate percentages of phones sold.

Year	Approximate percentage of phones sold					Total
	TalkEZ	TXT2	Cre8	Njoy	Others	
2000						100%
2002						100%

2. Between 2000 and 2002, which company:

   (a) increased its share of sales the most? _____

   (b) reduced its share of sales the most? _____

3. Is it true to say that TXT2 sold more phones in 2000 than in 2002? Explain your answer.

_____

_____

4. 🖩 In 2000, 6 million mobile phones were sold in total. In 2002, the total was 9.4 million. Complete this table to show the approximate **numbers** of phones sold.

Year	Approximate number of phones sold (millions)					Total
	TalkEZ	TXT2	Cre8	Njoy	Others	(millions)
2000						6
2002						9.4

NOW TRY THIS!

In 2003, Cre8 doubled its number of sales from 2002 and Njoy halved the number it sold. TalkEZ sold the same proportion of phones as it did in 2002. TXT2 changed its name to BTW and sold the largest proportion of the total number of phones sold.

● Sketch and label a pie chart to show the possible proportions of phones sold in 2003.

 When you find a percentage of a total, remember that the % sign stands for 'out of 100' or 'divided by 100'. Divide the percentage by 100 and multiply this by the total number (for example, 30% of 9.4 can be found like this: 30 ÷ 100 × 9.4).

TV viewing

A Look carefully at the information in this table.

Average time spent viewing television, video and DVD by region and sex, 2000

Region of England	Minutes per day		
	Male	Female	All
Northeast	208	187	197
Northwest	188	168	179
Yorkshire and the Humber	188	170	179
East Midlands	167	163	165
West Midlands	184	162	173
East	161	155	158
London	158	151	154
Southeast	163	149	156
Southwest	169	157	163

Source: UK 2000 Time Use Survey, Office for National Statistics

1. In which region is the average viewing time:

(a) highest for males? _____

(b) highest for females? _____

(c) lowest for males? _____

(d) lowest for females? _____

(e) highest for all? _____

(f) lowest for all? _____

2. What is the average daily viewing time for males in:

(a) the West Midlands? _____

(b) the Southwest? _____

3. What is the average daily viewing time for females in:

(a) London? _____

(b) the Northwest? _____

4. Which region shows the greatest difference between the average daily viewing time of males and females? _____

B

1. What is the daily **mean average** viewing time in the whole of England for:

(a) males? _____ **(b)** females? _____ **(c)** all? _____

Round your answers to the nearest whole number.

2. Compare the mean average viewing times for England with these times. Write what you notice.

	Male	Female	All
Wales	191	166	179
Scotland	192	170	180
Northern Ireland	157	146	152

_____

_____

_____

3. If you were asked to graph this data, what type of graph would you choose? _____

To calculate the **mean average**, find the total of all the values and divide by the number of values.

Developing Numeracy
Handling Data
Year 8
© A & C BLACK

TV viewing

C Look carefully at the information in this table.

Average time spent viewing television, video and DVD by region and sex, 2000

Region	Minutes per day		
	Male	Female	All
Northeast	208	187	197
Northwest	188	168	179
Yorkshire and the Humber	188	170	179
East Midlands	167	163	165
West Midlands	184	162	173
East	161	155	158
London	158	151	154
Southeast	163	149	156
Southwest	169	157	163
Wales	191	166	179
Scotland	192	170	180
Northern Ireland	157	146	152

Source: UK 2000 Time Use Survey, Office for National Statistics

1. Compare the viewing figures for males and females. What do you notice?

2. **(a)** Compare the viewing figures for London and southern England with northern England and Scotland. Describe what you notice.

   (b) Explain possible reasons for this.

3. Complete this table.

	Average viewing times		
	Mean	Median	Range
Males in UK			
Females in UK			
All in UK			

Round your answers to the nearest whole number.

NOW TRY THIS!

- Write a newspaper report about the differences in viewing habits of males and females across the UK. Use the answers to the questions above in your report.

 To calculate the **mean average**, find the total of all the values and divide by the number of values. Remember, the **median** is the middle value when the values are arranged in order. If there are two values in the middle, the median is halfway between the two. The **range** is the difference between the lowest value and the highest value.

Developing Numeracy
Handling Data
Year 8
© A & C BLACK

World records

A This table shows the world records for the men's 100 m sprint.

Sprint time (seconds)	Athlete	Year
12	Tom Burke	1896
10.8	Reggie Walker	1908
10.3	Jesse Owens	1936
9.95	Jim Hines	1968
9.93	Calvin Smith	1983
9.92	Carl Lewis	1988
9.90	Leroy Burrell	1990
9.86	Carl Lewis	1991
9.85	Leroy Burrell	1994
9.84	Donovan Bailey	1996
9.79	Maurice Greene	1999
9.78	Tim Montgomery	2002

1. By how many seconds is the 2002 world record faster than that of:

   (a) 1994? _0.07_

   (b) 1968? _____

   (c) 1896? _____

2. For how many years was the world record held by:

   (a) Tom Burke? _____

   (b) Jesse Owens? _____

   (c) Jim Hines? _____

   (d) Donovan Bailey? _____

3. Why do you think the record in 1896 was measured in whole seconds? _____

   _____

4. Between which two years did world records start to be measured in hundredths of a second?

   _____ and _____

B 1. Plot each world record on this graph. Mark the points with crosses, but do not join the crosses with a line.

2. On a separate piece of paper, write a report describing how the world record has changed.

In recent years, the world record has fallen more frequently, but by smaller amounts. Give possible reasons for this.

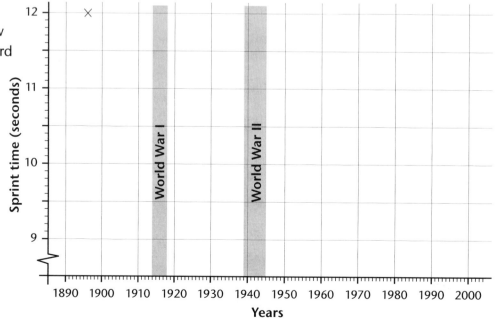

A zig-zag on the vertical axis of a graph shows that the scale has been interrupted. In part B, the lower part of the scale is squeezed because the sprint times between 0 and 9 seconds do not occur.

Developing Numeracy
Handling Data
Year 8
© A & C BLACK

40

World records

C

This table shows the fastest times over 100 m of different animals.

Animal	Time to travel 100 m (seconds)
Cheetah	3.20
Lion	4.47
Greyhound	4.97
Reindeer	6.99
Grizzly bear	7.46
African elephant	8.94
Black mamba	11.18
Pig	20.35
Snail	7452

On 14 September 2002, Tim Montgomery broke the men's 100 m sprint world record to become the fastest man on the planet. His time of 9.78 seconds beat the previous record by 0.01 seconds.

This is the same as 2 hours, 4 minutes and 12 seconds!

1. How much faster than Tim Montgomery's world record is each of these animals?

   (a) cheetah _6.58 sec_   **(b)** lion _____

   (c) greyhound _____   **(d)** reindeer _____

   (e) grizzly bear _____   **(f)** African elephant _____

2. Imagine Tim Montgomery and a cheetah had a race. If the cheetah kept running and ran each 100 m at 3.20 seconds, approximately how far would it travel by the time Tim crossed the 100 m finish line? _____

3. Imagine the lion and the pig had a race. If the lion kept running and ran each 100 m at 4.47 seconds, approximately how far would it travel by the time the pig crossed the 100 m finish line?

   _____

4. Imagine the pig and the snail had a race. If the pig kept running and ran each 100 m at 20.35 seconds, approximately how far would it travel by the time the snail crossed the 100 m finish line?

   _____

5. What might the 100 m record be for these animals? Discuss your answers with a partner.

   (a) hare _____   **(b)** horse _____   **(c)** mouse _____

NOW TRY THIS!

- Imagine there was a relay race between two teams of three animals. Each animal runs 100 m. Choose the teams so that the total times over 300 m are as close as possible to each other.

Remember that distance = speed × time. Find the speed in metres per second and multiply it by the time.

A bird in the hand...

A A survey investigated the clutch sizes of two species of garden birds. The survey looked at 300 breeding birds of each species.

The clutch size is the number of chicks hatched at the same time.

Garden warbler

Number of chicks in clutch	1	2	3	4	5	6	7	8
Frequency	0	6	21	120	144	9	0	0

Lesser whitethroat

Number of chicks in clutch	1	2	3	4	5	6	7	8
Frequency	0	6	9	60	207	12	0	6

1. Find the **modal number** of chicks per clutch for the:

   (a) garden warbler _____   **(b)** lesser whitethroat _____

   Explain why the mode is not very useful for comparing these distributions .

   _____

2. Find the **range** of the number of chicks per clutch for the:

   (a) garden warbler _____   **(b)** lesser whitethroat _____

   Explain what this information tells you about the clutch sizes of these birds.

   _____
   _____
   _____

B

1. Complete these tables to help you find the **mean** clutch size.

Garden warbler

Number of chicks in clutch	1	2	3	4	5	6	7	8	Total
Frequency	0	6	21	120	144	9	0	0	300
Number of chicks	0	12							

Mean number of chicks per clutch = _____

Lesser whitethroat

Number of chicks in clutch	1	2	3	4	5	6	7	8	Total
Frequency	0	6	9	60	207	12	0	6	
Number of chicks									

Mean number of chicks per clutch = _____

2. Write a description comparing the clutch sizes of the two species.

   _____
   _____

Refer to the mean and the range.

Remember, the **modal number** is the most common value. The **distribution** of a set of data is the way in which values in the set are spread between the minimum and maximum values. To find the **mean**, divide the total number of chicks by the number of clutches. Multiply the data in the frequency table to help you find this information.

**Developing Numeracy
Handling Data
Year 8
© A & C BLACK**

C

A survey investigated the clutch sizes of four species of garden birds. The survey looked at 300 breeding birds of each species.

Blackcap

Number of chicks in clutch	1	2	3	4	5	6	7	8	Total
Frequency	0	6	18	72	192	9	3	0	
Number of chicks									

Garden warbler

Number of chicks in clutch	1	2	3	4	5	6	7	8	Total
Frequency	0	6	21	120	144	9	0	0	
Number of chicks									

Whitethroat

Number of chicks in clutch	1	2	3	4	5	6	7	8	Total
Frequency	3	6	12	75	186	15	3	0	
Number of chicks									

Lesser whitethroat

Number of chicks in clutch	1	2	3	4	5	6	7	8	Total
Frequency	0	6	9	60	207	12	0	6	
Number of chicks									

1. Find the **modal number** of chicks per clutch for the:

   (a) blackcap _____   **(b)** garden warbler _____

   (c) whitethroat _____   **(d)** lesser whitethroat _____

   Explain why the mode is not very useful for comparing these **distributions**.

2. Find the **range** of the number of chicks per clutch for the:

   (a) blackcap _____   **(b)** garden warbler _____

   (c) whitethroat _____   **(d)** lesser whitethroat _____

3. Find the **mean** number of chicks per clutch for the:

   (a) blackcap _____   **(b)** garden warbler _____

   (c) whitethroat _____   **(d)** lesser whitethroat _____

NOW TRY THIS!

- Write a report explaining what this information tells you about the clutch sizes of these birds.
- The clutch size of another species has a mean of 4.8 and a range of 3. Compare this new species with the species above.

Remember, the **modal number** is the most common value. The **distribution** of a set of data is the way in which values in the set are spread between the minimum and maximum values. To find the **mean**, divide the total number of chicks by the number of clutches. Multiply the data in the frequency table to help you find this information.

Crime figures

A

Look at graph A.

1. What **percentage** of the offences was:

(a) 'Other theft'? _____

(b) 'Burglary'? _____

2. What **fraction** of the offences was:

(a) 'Theft of and from motor vehicles'? _____

(b) 'Drug offences'? _____

Look at graph B.

3. At what age is the number of:

(a) male offenders per 100 highest? _____

(b) female offenders per 100 highest? _____

4. Approximately how many males per 100 are convicted or cautioned at the age of:

(a) 16? _6_

(b) 26? _____

(c) 36? _____

(d) 46? _____

5. Approximately how many females per 100 are convicted or cautioned at the age of:

(a) 16? _____

(b) 26? _____

(c) 36? _____

(d) 46? _____

6. Is it true to say that no people over 70 are convicted or cautioned? Explain your answer.

_____

7. One in every 100 males are convicted or cautioned at what ages? _____ and _____

8. One in every 100 females are convicted or cautioned at what ages? _____ and _____

B

Look at graph C.

1. Approximately how many million crimes were recorded in:

(a) 88–89? _3.75_

(b) 91–92? _____

(c) 95–96? _____

(d) 97–98? _____

2. In which year was the number of recorded crimes:

(a) the highest? _____

(b) the lowest? _____

3. Look at the number of crimes 'cleared up' each year. Write what you notice.

_____

Look at graph D.

4. Which type of crime is:

(a) reported the most?

_____

(b) reported the least?

_____

(c) most unreported?

_____

(d) least unreported?

_____

5. Suggest reasons why crimes might not be reported. _____

_____

6. Is it true to say that more crimes go unreported than are reported? _____

When a crime is 'cleared up', this means that the police have identified the
offender. Graph D shows that some reported crimes are not recorded by
the police. This is often because the person who reported the crime
decides not to take the matter further.

Developing Numeracy
Handling Data
Year 8
© A & C BLACK

Crime figures

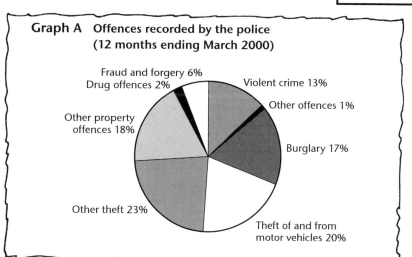

C These graphs show information about crime in England and Wales.

Work with a partner to decide what each graph tells you.

Graph A Offences recorded by the police (12 months ending March 2000)

Fraud and forgery 6%
Drug offences 2%
Other property offences 18%
Other theft 23%
Theft of and from motor vehicles 20%
Burglary 17%
Other offences 1%
Violent crime 13%

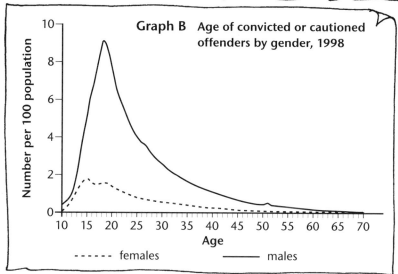

Graph B Age of convicted or cautioned offenders by gender, 1998

Number per 100 population (y-axis: 0 to 10)
Age (x-axis: 10 to 70)

----- females ——— males

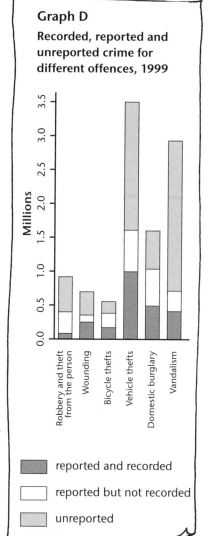

Graph D

Recorded, reported and unreported crime for different offences, 1999

Millions (y-axis: 0.0 to 3.5)

Robbery and theft from the person
Wounding
Bicycle thefts
Vehicle thefts
Domestic burglary
Vandalism

■ reported and recorded
□ reported but not recorded
▨ unreported

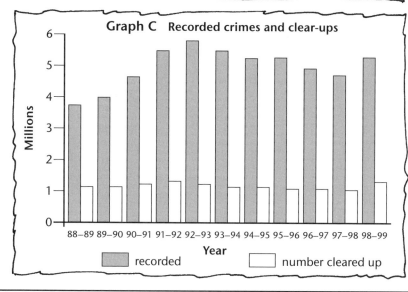

Graph C Recorded crimes and clear-ups

Millions (y-axis: 0 to 6)

88–89 89–90 90–91 91–92 92–93 93–94 94–95 95–96 96–97 97–98 98–99
Year

▨ recorded   □ number cleared up

NOW TRY THIS!

- For each graph, write a report saying what conclusions you can draw from the information. Point out anything interesting or unusual. Suggest possible reasons or explanations for the trends.

Read each graph title carefully and make sure you know what each axis shows. Look at the scales and the shape of the graph. When a crime is 'cleared up', this means that the police have identified the offender. Some reported crimes are not recorded by the police. This is often because the person who reported the crime decides not to take the matter further.

Visiting times

A

This bar chart shows data about tourists and tourism in the UK.

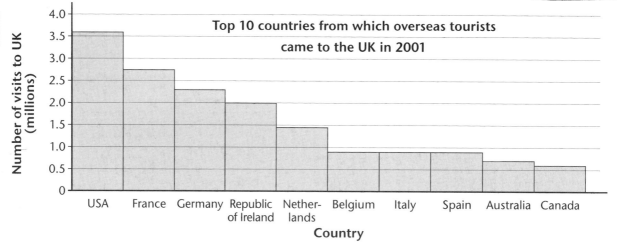

Top 10 countries from which overseas tourists came to the UK in 2001

Number of visits to UK (millions)

USA France Germany Republic of Ireland Netherlands Belgium Italy Spain Australia Canada

Country

Tourists came to the UK from overseas for a total of 22.8 million visits in 2001.

1. Approximately how many million visits were from:

   (a) France? _2.75_   **(b)** the Netherlands? _____

   (c) Australia? _____   **(d)** the Republic of Ireland? _____

   (e) Italy? _____   **(f)** countries not listed? _____

> To answer question (f), find the total number of visits by the top 10 countries, then subtract this from 22.8 million.

2. Approximately what **percentage** (to 1 d.p.) of the **total** overseas visits were from:

   (a) the USA? _____   **(b)** Germany? _____   **(c)** Canada? _____

B

The table shows the approximate amount of money spent by overseas visitors in 2001.

Overseas tourists spent a total of £11 300 million in 2001.

Country	£ millions
USA	2400
France	680
Germany	730
Republic of Ireland	550
Netherlands	390
Belgium	150
Italy	420
Spain	320
Australia	540
Canada	320

1. Use this, and the data from part A, to find out:

   (a) which overseas visitors tend to spend the **most** per visit _____

   (b) which overseas visitors tend to spend the **least** per visit _____

   (c) the amount spent per visit by tourists from countries not listed _____

2. Write a report about the information on this page. Draw other graphs or charts to support your findings.

To find what percentage of the total overseas visits are from a particular country, find that country's number of visits and divide it by the total number of visits. Then multiply this by 100 to get a percentage.

Developing Numeracy
Handling Data
Year 8
© A & C BLACK

Visiting times

Interpret graphs and draw inferences

C Look carefully at this graph.

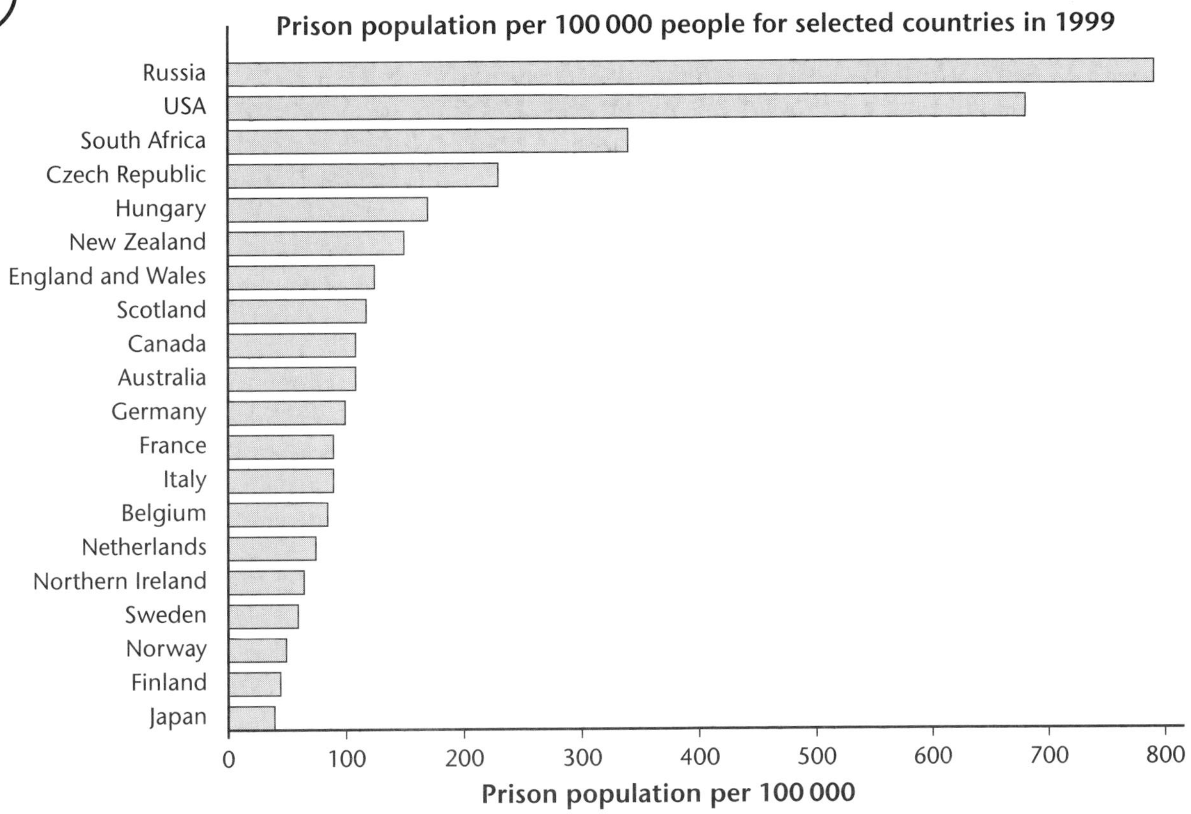

Prison population per 100 000 people for selected countries in 1999
Russia
USA
South Africa
Czech Republic
Hungary
New Zealand
England and Wales
Scotland
Canada
Australia
Germany
France
Italy
Belgium
Netherlands
Northern Ireland
Sweden
Norway
Finland
Japan
0
100
200
300
400
500
600
700
800
Prison population per 100 000

1. In 1999, approximately how many people per 100 000 were in prison in:

(a) Russia? ________ **(b)** the USA? ________ **(c)** England and Wales? ________

(d) Australia? ________ **(e)** the Netherlands? ________ **(f)** Japan? ________

2. Is it true to say that there must be more crime in Russia than in Sweden? Explain your answer.

____

____

3. In 1999, there were over 200 times as many prisoners in Japan as in Norway. Explain how this could be possible.

____

____

NOW TRY THIS!

This table shows the populations of several countries in 1999.

- Work with a partner to find the approximate number of prisoners in each country.
- Plan a presentation about the information on this page, using some of your answers.

Country	Population
Germany	82 million
France	59 million
England and Wales	53 million
Canada	31 million
Sweden	9 million
Japan	126 million

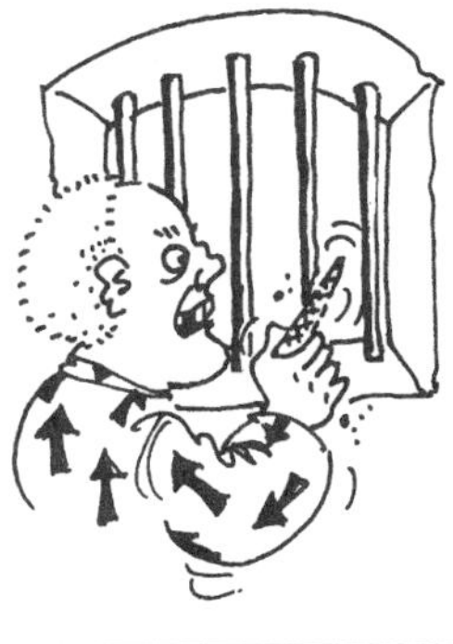

When you plan a presentation, make sure you give the key information and discuss what the data might indicate. Make your own suggestions to explain the trends.

Would you chance it?

A Work with a partner. Write two events for each of these probability words.

Remember, an **even chance** is the same as 50:50.

!

certain   *Bonfire night will be on 5 November.*

likely

even chance

unlikely

impossible

B This is a game for two players. The cards show the probabilities of winning money on different slot machines.

☆ Player 1: choose a card.

☆ Player 2: try to find a card with the same probability. If you are correct, score a point and cross out the cards. If you are incorrect, Player 1 scores a point.

☆ Take turns to choose cards and continue the game.

☆ The winner is the player with the most points when all the cards are crossed out.

$\frac{1}{5}$	75%	$\frac{3}{10}$	$\frac{1}{3}$	$\frac{1}{25}$
50%	0.3	$\frac{3}{4}$	40%	$\frac{1}{2}$
$\frac{2}{5}$	20%	0.4	$\frac{4}{12}$	$\frac{4}{10}$
$\frac{1}{4}$	4%	$\frac{3}{5}$	25%	0.6

 Probabilities can be written as fractions, decimals or percentages. The denominator (bottom number) of a fraction is the total number of possible outcomes. The numerator (top number) shows the number of outcomes being described: for example, $\frac{1}{5}$ means that the probability of winning is one go in every five.

Developing Numeracy
Handling Data
Year 8
© A & C BLACK

48

Would you chance it?

Two boxes contain different numbers of milk chocolates and dark chocolates.

Box 1
6 milk chocolates
9 dark chocolates

Box 2
4 milk chocolates
8 dark chocolates

1. Ellie likes milk chocolates. If she picks only one chocolate at random from one box, which box should she choose? Why? _____

_____

2. Ellie is offered a third box of chocolates containing 8 milk chocolates and 12 dark chocolates. Which box should she choose now? Why? _____

_____

Estate 1

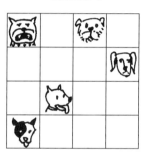

Estate 2

Estate 3

Each small square represents a house on a housing estate. The houses with dogs are shown. The postwoman must visit one house on each estate to deliver a parcel.

3. What is the probability that the postwoman will meet a dog on:

   (a) Estate 1? $\frac{5}{16}$ **(b)** Estate 2? _____   **(c)** Estate 3? _____

4. Which of these probabilities is the greatest? _____

5. What is the probability that she will *not* meet a dog on:

   (a) Estate 1? _____   **(b)** Estate 2? _____   **(c)** Estate 3? _____

6. Explain how you worked out the answers to question 5.

_____

_____

_____

NOW TRY THIS!

- Design a housing estate where the probability of meeting a dog lies between the probabilities of Estates 2 and 3.

The denominator (bottom number) of a fraction is the total number of possible outcomes. The numerator (top number) shows the number of outcomes being described: for example, 4 out of 12 houses is written as $\frac{4}{12}$ or $\frac{1}{3}$ (simplify fractions if you can).

Probability play

A

Here is a full pack of cards (without jokers). The **suits** are clubs, diamonds, hearts and spades.

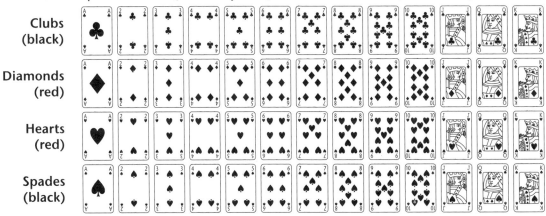

Clubs (black)

Diamonds (red)

Hearts (red)

Spades (black)

1. Give the number of:

(a) cards _____   (b) suits _____   (c) red cards _____

(d) hearts _____   (e) picture cards _____   (f) aces _____

2. What is the probability that a card chosen at random will be: (a) a club? _____

(b) a black card? _____   (c) an ace? _____   (d) an odd number? _____

(e) a picture card? _____   (f) either a 2 or a 4? _____

(g) a multiple of 3? _____   (h) a multiple of 5? _____

(i) an odd numbered red card? _____   (j) a number less than 6? _____

> Here, the aces and picture cards do not count as numbers. !

B

1. What is the probability that a card chosen at random will *not* be: (a) a club? _____

(b) a black card? _____   (c) an ace? _____   (d) an odd number? _____

(e) a picture card? _____   (f) either a 2 or a 4? _____

(g) a multiple of 3? _____   (h) a multiple of 5? _____

(i) an odd numbered red card? _____   (j) a number less than 6? _____

2. (a) Complete this pattern.

Probability of <u>an ace</u>	+ probability of ___*not an ace*___	= certain	
$\frac{1}{13}$	+	= _____	
Probability of <u>a club</u>	+ probability of _____	= certain	
_____	+ _____	= _____	
Probability of <u>a red card</u>	+ probability of _____	= certain	
_____	+ _____	= _____	

(b) Discuss with a partner what you notice.

 The denominator (bottom number) of a fraction is the total number of possible outcomes. The numerator (top number) shows the number of outcomes being described: for example, 4 out of 52 cards is written as $\frac{4}{52}$ or $\frac{1}{13}$ (simplify fractions if you can).

Probability play

Here is a full set of children's plastic shapes. Colour the shapes as shown.

Thick shapes **Thin shapes**

Red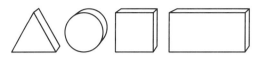

Blue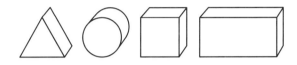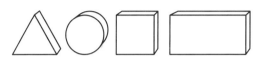

Yellow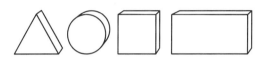

1. Give the number of:

   (a) shapes _____   **(b)** red shapes _____   **(c)** cylinders _____

   (d) thick shapes _____   **(e)** cuboids (square and rectangular prisms) _____

   (f) blue triangular prisms _____   **(g)** thin yellow square prisms _____

2. What is the probability that a shape chosen at random will be:

   (a) blue? _____   **(b)** thick? _____   **(c)** a shape that is *not* red? _____

   (d) a triangular prism? _____   **(e)** a yellow cylinder? _____   **(f)** a thick cuboid? _____

   (g) a blue or yellow cuboid? _____   **(h)** thin and yellow? _____

   (i) a thin, red cylinder? _____   **(j)** a shape that is *not* a cuboid? _____

   (k) a thick shape with straight sides? _____

3. What is the probability that a shape chosen at random will *not* be:

   (a) blue? _____   **(b)** thick? _____   **(c)** a shape that is *not* red? _____

   (d) a triangular prism? _____   **(e)** a yellow cylinder? _____   **(f)** a thick cuboid? _____

   (g) a blue or yellow cuboid? _____   **(h)** thin and yellow? _____

   (i) a thin, red cylinder? _____   **(j)** a shape that is *not* a cuboid? _____

   (k) a thick shape with straight sides? _____

NOW TRY THIS!

A different set is made up of 12 thin triangular prisms, square prisms and cylinders.
It has the following probabilities, when one shape is picked at random:

Probability of it being red = $\frac{1}{4}$ Probability of it being a square prism = $\frac{1}{3}$

Probability of it *not* being a cylinder = $\frac{5}{6}$ Probability of it being yellow = $\frac{3}{4}$

- Draw the set of 12 thin shapes. Some shapes might be identical.

- Make up your own puzzle like this for a partner to solve.

Different answers are possible. **!**

 The denominator (bottom number) of a fraction is the total number of possible outcomes. The numerator (top number) shows the number of outcomes being described: for example, 8 out of 24 shapes is written as $\frac{8}{24}$ or $\frac{1}{3}$ (simplify fractions if you can).

Domino dilemmas

A Here is a full set of dominoes.

1. Give the number of:

   (a) dominoes altogether _____

   (b) dominoes with a total of 6 _____

   (c) dominoes with at least one blank _____

   (d) doubles (same on both sides) _____

   (e) dominoes with a total of 12 _____

2. What is the probability that a domino chosen at random will:

   (a) be a double? _____   **(b)** have at least one blank? _____   **(c)** have at least 1 six? _____

   (d) have two blanks? _____   **(e)** have a total of 12? _____   **(f)** have an odd total? _____

   (g) have a total of 4? _____   **(h)** have a total of 7? _____

   (i) have a total greater than 5? _____   **(j)** have a total less than 4? _____

3. What is the probability that a domino chosen at random will *not*:

   (a) be a double? _____   **(b)** have at least one blank? _____   **(c)** have at least 1 six? _____

   (d) have two blanks? _____   **(e)** have a total of 12? _____   **(f)** have an odd total? _____

   (g) have a total of 4? _____   **(h)** have a total of 7? _____

   (i) have a total greater than 5? _____   **(j)** have a total less than 4? _____

B All the dominoes with a total of 6 are removed from the set.
The remaining dominoes are put in a bag.

> First work out how many dominoes are in the new set.

!

What is the probability that a domino chosen at random from this bag will:

   (a) be a double? _____   **(b)** have at least one blank? _____   **(c)** have at least 1 six? _____

   (d) have two blanks? _____   **(e)** have a total of 12? _____   **(f)** have an odd total? _____

   (g) have a total of 4? _____   **(h)** have a total of 7? _____

   (i) have a total greater than 5? _____   **(j)** have a total less than 4? _____

The denominator (bottom number) of a fraction is the total number of possible outcomes. The numerator (top number) shows the number of outcomes being described: for example, 7 out of 28 dominoes is written as $\frac{7}{28}$ or $\frac{1}{4}$ (simplify fractions if you can).

Developing Numeracy
Handling Data
Year 8
© A & C BLACK

Domino dilemmas

C

1. A full set of dominoes is put into a bag.

Two dominoes are chosen from a second full set. These are also put in the bag.

The following probabilities are **true**.

The probability that a domino chosen at random from this bag will...

...have at least 1 six is $\frac{7}{30}$

...have at least 1 one is $\frac{7}{30}$

...have a total of 6 is $\frac{4}{30}$ or $\frac{2}{15}$

...have a total of 4 is $\frac{4}{30}$ or $\frac{2}{15}$

...have a total of 7 is $\frac{4}{30}$ or $\frac{2}{15}$

...be a double is $\frac{8}{30}$ or $\frac{4}{15}$

...have at least 1 two is $\frac{9}{30}$

...have at least one blank is $\frac{7}{30}$

Work out which two dominoes were added to the bag.

2. Two dominoes are chosen from a third full set. These are added to the same bag (which still contains the extra two dominoes from the last question).

The following probabilities are now **true**.

The probability that a domino chosen at random from this bag will...

...have at least 1 six is $\frac{8}{32}$ or $\frac{1}{4}$

...have at least one blank is $\frac{8}{32}$ or $\frac{1}{4}$

...have a total of 12 is $\frac{2}{32}$ or $\frac{1}{16}$

...have a total of 1 is $\frac{2}{32}$ or $\frac{1}{16}$

...have a total of 0 is $\frac{1}{32}$

...be a double is $\frac{9}{32}$

...have at least 1 five is $\frac{8}{32}$ or $\frac{1}{4}$

...have at least 1 four is $\frac{7}{32}$

Work out which two dominoes were added to the bag.

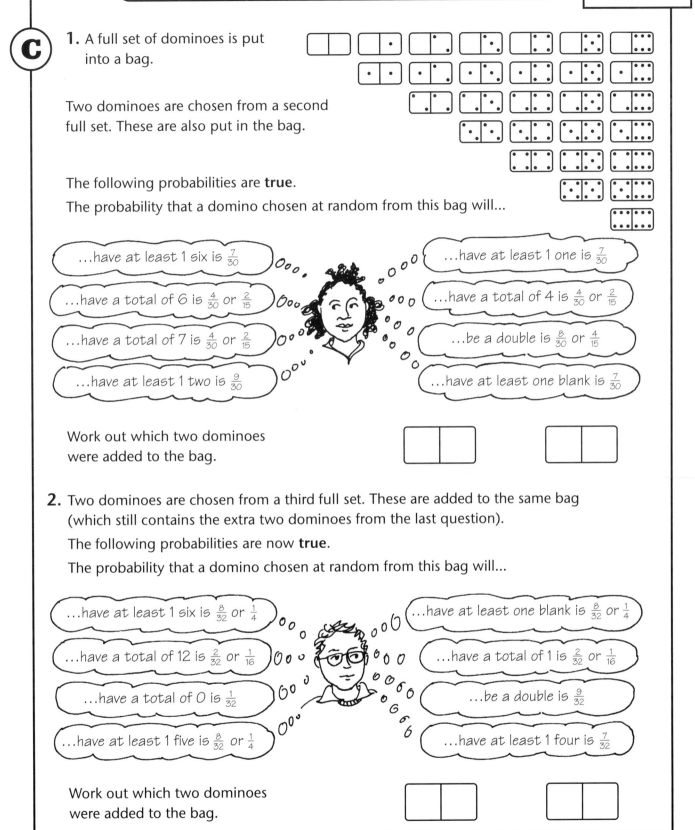

NOW TRY THIS!

- Imagine you have a full set of dominoes. You then choose two more dominoes from another full set. Write statements to make a puzzle like the one above. Give it to a partner to solve.

You will have **30** dominoes in your set altogether. **!**

 The denominator (bottom number) of a fraction is the total number of possible outcomes. The numerator (top number) shows the number of outcomes being described: for example, 4 out of 30 dominoes is written as $\frac{4}{30}$ or $\frac{2}{15}$ (simplify fractions if you can).

**Developing Numeracy
Handling Data
Year 8**
© A & C BLACK

53

In a spin

A 1. List all four possible outcomes of each event.

(a) A mother gives birth to twins.

Child 1	Child 2
male	female
male	

(b) Two coins are tossed and land flat.

Coin 1	Coin 2
heads	

(c) A pair of red socks and a pair of blue socks are in a drawer. Two socks are chosen at random.

Sock 1	Sock 2
red	

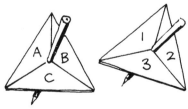

(d) You play two tennis matches where you win or lose.

Match 1	Match 2
win	

2. List all the possible outcomes of these events.

(a) A person chooses two pizza toppings from ham, mushroom or pineapple.

ham and mushroom,

(b) A person makes a sandwich with one type of bread and one filling. There is a choice of brown or white bread. The fillings are cheese, honey or jam.

brown with cheese,

B 1. List all the possible outcomes when these two spinners are spun together.

A1,

2. What is the probability of:

(a) spinning A2? _____   **(b)** spinning C3? _____   **(c)** spinning the letter B? _____

(d) spinning an odd number? _____   **(e)** *not* spinning the letter C? _____

(f) spinning a number less than 3? _____   **(g)** *not* spinning a number less than 3? _____

 When you record the outcomes of an event, such as tossing two coins, call the coins Coin 1 and Coin 2 so that you can see which coin was heads and which was tails.

**Developing Numeracy
Handling Data
Year 8**
© A & C BLACK

C

1. These two spinners are spun together. List the possible outcomes in the table.

	A	B	C	D
1	A1			
2				
3				
4				

What is the probability of:

(a) spinning A2? _____

(b) spinning the letter B? _____

(c) *not* spinning a 3? _____   **(d)** spinning an even number? _____

(e) *not* spinning a C or a 4? _____   **(f)** *not* spinning a C or an odd number? _____

2. These two spinners are spun together and the total is found. Complete the table.

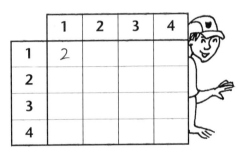

	1	2	3	4
1	2			
2				
3				
4				

What is the probability of:

(a) spinning a total of 5? _____

(b) spinning an even total? _____

(c) *not* spinning a total of 7? _____   **(d)** spinning a total of 3 or 4? _____

(e) spinning a total greater than 4? _____   **(f)** *not* spinning a total of 6? _____

(g) *not* spinning a total of 2 or 3? _____   **(h)** *not* spinning a total less than 5? _____

3. These two spinners are spun together and the total is found. Complete the table.

What is the probability of:

(a) spinning a total of 11? _____

(b) spinning an even total? _____

(c) *not* spinning a total of 9 or 11? _____

(d) *not* spinning a total greater than 6? _____   **(e)** spinning a total less than 3? _____

NOW TRY THIS!

You have two dice. One of them is numbered 1 to 6 and the other is numbered 7 to 12.

● What do you think the most common total score will be?

● Draw a table to show all the possible outcomes when both dice are thrown together.

● Was your prediction correct? Explain why.

 Remember to simplify fractions if you can.

Test it!

A

Work with a partner. You need one suit from a pack of cards. Shuffle it before you begin.

☆ One person holds out the cards, face down. The other person picks one card.
☆ Record which card is picked. Then put it back with the others.
☆ Shuffle the cards and repeat the experiment. Do this 50 times.

> Use tallying to record the results. **!**

1. Record your results in this table.

A	2	3	4	5	6	7	8	9	10	J	Q	K

2. From your results, give the │ experimental probability │ of picking:

    (a) an ace _____   **(b)** a picture card _____   **(c)** an even number _____

    (d) a 4 _____   **(e)** a Jack _____   **(f)** a numbered card (not including aces) _____

> The **theoretical probability** is based on equally likely outcomes, rather than on experimental results.

3. Give the theoretical probability of picking:

    (a) an ace _____   **(b)** a picture card _____   **(c)** an even number _____

    (d) a 4 _____   **(e)** a Jack _____   **(f)** a numbered card (not including aces) _____

4. Are the experimental and theoretical probabilities the same? Give reasons for this.

_____

_____

B

1. Now join with another pair in your class. Add their results to yours and record the totals in this table.

A	2	3	4	5	6	7	8	9	10	J	Q	K

2. From these results, give the **experimental probability** of picking:

    (a) an ace _____   **(b)** a picture card _____   **(c)** an even number _____

    (d) a 4 _____   **(e)** a Jack _____   **(f)** a numbered card (not including aces) _____

3. Are these experimental probabilities closer to the theoretical probabilities you worked out in part A? Give reasons for this. _____

_____

_____

4. Using the results above, predict the number of times you would expect to get a 7, if you picked a card:

    (a) 200 times _____   **(b)** 500 times _____   **(c)** 1000 times _____

In part A, use just one suit – clubs, diamonds, hearts or spades. The **experimental probability** is the probability you work out using the results of an experiment. You can calculate the **theoretical probability** based on equally likely outcomes. The more times you do an experiment, the more likely the results are to match the theoretical probability.

Developing Numeracy
Handling Data
Year 8
© A & C BLACK

Test it!

C Work with a partner. You need one matchstick (or cocktail stick) and a large sheet of paper.

☆ On your piece of paper, draw parallel lines that are the same distance apart as the length of your stick (for example, if you use a matchstick 4 cm long, you should draw parallel lines 4 cm apart).

☆ Place your piece of paper on the floor next to a table.

☆ Now drop your stick from table height onto the piece of paper.

☆ Record whether your stick lands on a line or between lines.

☆ If the stick misses the paper, do not count it and drop it again.

☆ Record the results of **50** drops.

1. Record your results here:

	Tally	Frequency
On a line		
Between lines		
		Total = 50

From your results, give the **experimental probability** of the stick landing:

(a) on a line _____   **(b)** between lines _____

2. Now join with another pair in your class. Add their results to yours and record them here:

From these results, give the experimental probability of the stick landing:

(a) on a line _____   **(b)** between lines _____

3. Find out the results of other pairs in your class. Add together *all* the results and record them here:

From these results, give the experimental probability of the stick landing:

(a) on a line _____   **(b)** between lines _____

NOW TRY THIS!

● Do another experiment. This time, draw parallel lines where the distance between the lines is *twice* the length of your stick.

Find probabilities for each of the | mutually exclusive outcomes |.
Write a report explaining what you have found out.

 The **experimental probability** is the probability you work out using the results of an experiment. **Mutually exclusive outcomes** are outcomes that cannot both occur in the same experiment: here a matchstick cannot land between lines and on a line at the same time.

It's one big lottery

Your teacher will call out the National Lottery results from the last eight draws. Write them on these balls.

(balls grid)

1. (a) Which number (or numbers) occurred most frequently? _____

(b) What is the total number of balls above? _____

2. Look *only* at the data from the last eight draws. Work out the **experimental probability** of the next ball picked:

(a) being the number 7 _____ **(b)** being a number from 1–9 _____

(c) being an even number _____ **(d)** being a number above 30 _____

(e) being the number 22 _____ **(f)** being a number in the 20s _____

(g) being a multiple of 5 _____ **(h)** being a number containing the digit 4 _____

(i) *not* being a multiple of 10 _____ **(j)** *not* being a prime number _____

(k) *not* being a square number _____ **(l)** *not* being the number 35 _____

1. There are 49 balls in the Lottery, numbered from 1 to 49. They are all equally likely to be picked. Write the **theoretical probability** of the next ball picked:

(a) being the number 7 _____ **(b)** being a number from 1–9 _____

(c) being an even number _____ **(d)** being a number above 30 _____

(e) being the number 22 _____ **(f)** being a number in the 20s _____

(g) being a multiple of 5 _____ **(h)** being a number containing the digit 4 _____

(i) *not* being a multiple of 10 _____ **(j)** *not* being a prime number _____

(k) *not* being a square number _____ **(l)** *not* being the number 35 _____

2. Are the experimental and theoretical probabilities the same? Give reasons for this.

_____

The **experimental probability** is the probability you work out using the results of an experiment. You can calculate the **theoretical probability** based on equally likely outcomes. The more times you do an experiment, the more likely the results are to match the theoretical probability. Remember to simplify fractions if you can.

Developing Numeracy
Handling Data
Year 8
© A & C BLACK

It's one big lottery

C Your teacher will call out the National Lottery results from the last draw.

1. Say whether you **agree** or **disagree** with each of these comments. Explain your thinking.

> For the next draw I *would not* choose the same numbers as the most recent draw, as those numbers are less likely to come up.

_____
_____
_____
_____

> For the next draw I *would* choose the same numbers as the most recent draw, as these are lucky numbers.

_____
_____
_____
_____

> For the next draw it makes no difference what numbers I pick, as they are all equally likely to come up.

_____
_____
_____
_____

2. This table shows the frequency of each number in past National Lottery draws.

1 = 89	2 = 99	3 = 86	4 = 86	5 = 83	6 = 91	7 = 94	8 = 84	9 = 92	10 = 93
11 = 99	12 = 92	13 = 72	14 = 93	15 = 83	16 = 80	17 = 84	18 = 89	19 = 91	20 = 78
21 = 76	22 = 81	23 = 105	24 = 87	25 = 103	26 = 87	27 = 96	28 = 100	29 = 90	30 = 94
31 = 104	32 = 104	33 = 90	34 = 85	35 = 92	36 = 94	37 = 84	38 = 116	39 = 79	40 = 100
41 = 77	42 = 83	43 = 105	44 = 111	45 = 92	46 = 94	47 = 102	48 = 93	49 = 82	

Which number (or numbers) occurred:

(a) most frequently? _____ **(b)** least frequently? _____

3. The table shows a total of 4464 balls picked.

(a) Out of this total, about how many times would you have expected each ball to be picked? _____

(b) Explain why the actual results do not match this expected frequency.

_____
_____
_____

- Does the Lottery number frequency table help you to decide which numbers to choose? Explain your answer.

You can calculate the **theoretical probability** based on equally likely outcomes. The more times you do an experiment, the more likely the results are to match the theoretical probability.

Answers

p 8

A Possible answers:
  (a) In both out-of-town shopping complexes and town centres, mix of shoppers
  (b) At school, pupils and teachers/other staff
  (c) At a library, elderly people
  (d) In a town centre, people of all ages

B Possible related questions:
  (b) Where can I find the data?
      Are more people born in summer?
  (c) What is 'value for money'?
      Do all have similar dishes for comparison?

p 18

A **(a)** 34
  (b) 34
  (c) 32.5
  (d) 33.125
  (e) 35.7

B1 **(a)**

0	1	2	3	4	5	6	7	8	Total
6	12	43	39	56	67	58	16	3	**300**
0	12	86	117	224	335	348	112	24	**1258**

(b) 4.19

B2 **(a)**

0	1	2	3	4	5	6	7	8	Total
0	3	17	78	79	88	91	5	1	**362**
0	3	34	234	316	440	546	35	8	**1616**

Mean score = **4.46**

(b)

0	1	2	3	4	5	6	7	8	Total
2	6	17	15	85	96	4	0	0	**225**
0	6	34	45	340	480	24	0	0	**929**

Mean score = **4.13**

(c)

0	1	2	3	4	5	6	7	8	Total
8	11	17	56	63	68	89	53	8	**373**
0	11	34	168	252	340	534	371	64	**1774**

Mean score = **4.76**

p 19

C2 **(a)** 25.2
  (b) 16.4
  (c) 62.6
  (d) 38.08

Now try this!
35.9

p 20

A1 Round 1: 94, 73, 73, 55
  Round 2: 87, 17, 67, 54
  Semi-final: 109, 87, 87, 66
  Final: 147, 52, 73, 62

B1 594

B2 **(a)** 27
  (b) 18.5
  (c) 88.75

B3 and **B4**
  The median is most representative. The mean is skewed by two results: 300 and 600.

p 21

C1

SUPERSPORTS

Cleaners (£25)	Assistants (£42)	Managers (£83)	Total
3	6	1	10
£75	£252	£83	£410

Bats'n'Balls

Cleaners (£28)	Assistants (£46)	Managers (£100)	Total
5	9	1	**15**
£140	£414	£100	**£654**

Sportsavers

Cleaners (£31)	Assistants (£59)	Managers (£124)	Total
12	15	3	**30**
£372	£885	£372	**£1629**

Sports 4 U

Cleaners (£24)	Assistants (£29)	Managers (£105)	Total
4	5	2	**11**
£96	£145	£210	**£451**

Focusports

Cleaners (£26)	Assistants (£54)	Managers (£101)	Total
8	7	2	**17**
£208	£378	£202	**£788**

Firstchoice Sports

Cleaners (£22)	Assistants (£32)	Managers (£205)	Total
4	3	2	**9**
£88	£96	£410	**£594**

C2 **(a)**

Supersports		Bats'n'Balls	
Range £58	Mode £42	Range £72	Mode £46
Median £42	Mean £41	Median £46	Mean £43.60
Sportsavers		**Sports 4 U**	
Range £93	Mode £59	Range £81	Mode £29
Median £59	Mean £54.30	Median £29	Mean £41
Focusports		**Firstchoice Sports**	
Range £75	Mode £26	Range £183	Mode £22
Median £54	Mean £46.35	Median £32	Mean £66